Other Titles of Interest

BP316 Practical Electronic Design Data

BP321 Circuit Source – Book 1

BP322 Circuit Source – Book 2

BP396 Electronic Hobbyists Data Book

PRACTICAL ELECTRONIC MODEL RAILWAY PROJECTS

by

R. A. PENFOLD

BERNARD BABANI (publishing) LTD
THE GRAMPIANS
SHEPHERDS BUSH ROAD
LONDON W6 7NF
ENGLAND

Please Note

© 1996 BERNARD BABANI (publishing) LTD

First Published – November 1996

British Library Cataloguing in Publication Data
A catalogue record for this book is available from the British Library

ISBN 0 85934 384 7

Cover Design by Gregor Arthur
Printed and bound in Great Britain by Cox & Wyman Ltd, Reading

Preface

Model railways have, of course, been very popular for many years now, and not only with the younger generation! Electronic gadgets for use with model railways are a relatively recent development, but they have been readily accepted by most model railway enthusiasts. Some electronic circuits can greatly enhance the capabilities of any model railway, from a simple oval of single track to a large and complex layout. Some simple electronic projects can provide a layout with much greater realism, and the user with a lot more fun.

The main aim of this book is to provide a number of useful but reasonably simple electronic projects for the model railway enthusiast. The projects featured include controllers, signals, and sound effects units. To help simplify construction, strip-board layouts and wiring diagrams are provided for all the projects featured in chapters one and two. These chapters respectively cover train controllers and accessories such as signals and sound effect units.

Using a PC as the basis of controllers and signalling systems is covered in chapter three. This chapter is not intended for beginners, and a basic understanding of electronics is needed in order to build and use these projects. In order to develop the projects and programs it is also necessary to have a reasonable understanding of computing and computer interfacing. Using a computer with a model railway is a very interesting avenue to pursue, and is one that I would certainly recommend to any model railway enthusiast who owns a suitable computer.

R. A. Penfold

Contents

Page

Chapter 1 – CONTROLLERS 1
  Performance 4
  Constant Voltage 6
  Constant Voltage Circuit 7
  Mains PSU 7
  Construction 10
  Heatsink 14
  PSU Construction 17
  In Use 20
  Pulse Control 23
  Pulse Controller Circuit 25
  Construction 28
  In Use 31
  "Improved" Pulsed Controller 32
  The Circuit 33
  Construction 35
  Pushbutton Control 39
  The Circuit 39
  Construction 44
  Customising 44
  Inertia Controller 45

Chapter 2 – ACCESSORIES 51
  To The Point 51
  The Circuit 54
  Multi-Point Control 57
  Automatic Signal 59
  The Circuit 61
  Construction 65
  Signal Controller 66
  The Circuit 67
  Construction 69
  Electronic Steam Whistle 72
  The Circuit 75
  Construction 78

Chapter 2 (Continued)   **Page**

Two Tone Horn 81
The Circuit 81
Construction 83
Automatic Train Horn 86
The Circuit 89
Construction 90
Automatic Chuffer 93
The Circuit 95
Construction 98
Manual Chuffer 102
Electronic Track "Cleaner" 106
The Circuit 108
Construction 110

Chapter 3 – COMPUTERISED LAYOUTS 115
Ins and Outs 115
Properly Addressed 118
I/O Line Address Mapping 119
Position Sensing 122
Signals 124
Train Controllers 132
Forward/Reverse 136
Software 140
Pulsed Controller 141
Software 143
P.W.M. Control 145
P.W.M. Circuit 148
5 Volt Supply 151

Chapter 1

CONTROLLERS

Model train controllers vary greatly in their cost and complexity. In general, the level of performance and number of features are reflected in a controller's cost. Very simple types often perform quite badly, and fail to give anything approaching realistic results however carefully they are used. Most basic controllers use one of the arrangements shown in Figure 1.1 or Figure 1.2.

If we consider the circuit of Figure 1.1 first, this has a step-down transformer (T1) to provide a low voltage output of about 15 volts a.c. from the 230 volt a.c. mains supply. It also provides isolation, so that it is safe to touch the wiring on the secondary side of T1. This is clearly essential in an application such as this, where the tracks connect to the controller, and the users are quite likely to come into contact with the tracks from time-to-time.

D1 to D4 form a bridge rectifier which converts the a.c. output from T1 into a pulsating d.c. signal. It only requires the addition of a capacitor to convert the pulsing d.c. signal to a reasonably "smooth" d.c. signal. In practice a smoothing capacitor is not usually included, because a small d.c. electric motor works perfectly well from a d.c. signal that is pulsing at 100Hz.

In a very basic controller this circuitry is replaced by batteries. Batteries do not provide a particularly satisfactory means of powering a model railway, since the current consumption of the average model locomotive is quite high at around 0.5 to one amp. This tends to give a short battery life and high running costs with "dry" batteries, and frequent recharging is needed with rechargeable batteries. The controller circuits featured in this book could be battery powered, but I would not recommend this.

The power fed to the train is controlled via a potentiometer (VR1), or "rheostat" as the higher power potentiometers are sometimes called. The potentiometer must be a high power type because the output currents involved in this application would almost instantly "zap" an ordinary type. With VR1 at

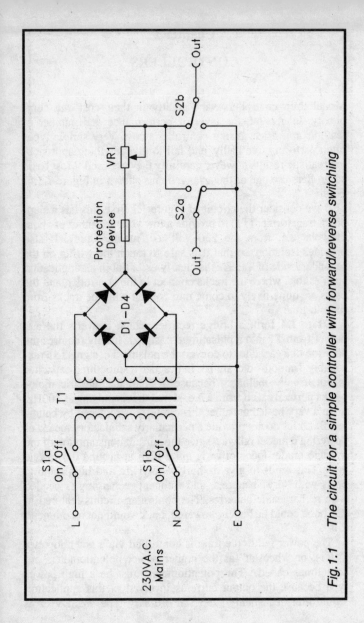

Fig.1.1   The circuit for a simple controller with forward/reverse switching

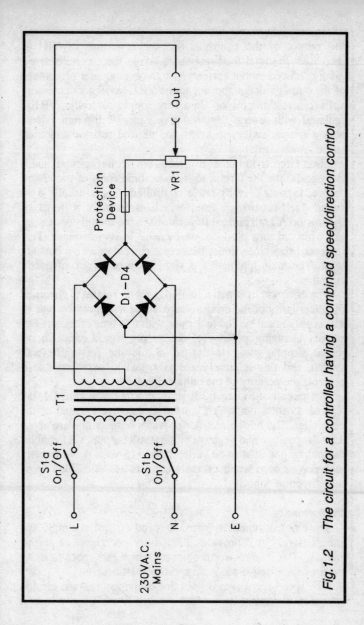

Fig.1.2   The circuit for a controller having a combined speed/direction control

L ○——
S1a
On/Off

230VA.C.
Mains

N ○——
S1b
On/Off

E ○——

T1

D1–D4

Protection
Device

VR1

C Out

minimum resistance the motor in the train receives the full output of the controller. As the resistance of VR1 is increased, the total load resistance across the controller rises, giving reduced output current. Also, an ever greater percentage of the output voltage appears across VR1, leaving a decreasing voltage across the motor. In a very simple controller, VR1 is replaced with several fixed value resistors of different values, plus a simple switch to select the desired resistor and train speed.

Short circuits and other overloads are not uncommon, and it is essential for the circuit to include some form of protection device. In simple ready-made controllers this is usually a so called "self-repairing" fuse, which is actually a form of thermistor. A high current flow results in the thermistor heating up, which in turn produces an increase in its resistance. This increased resistance limits the output current to a high but safe level. The main alternative is some form of electro-magnetic cutout.

The direction in which a small d.c. motor rotates is governed by the polarity of the drive voltage. It is for this reason that an a.c. supply is not suuitable for use with this type of motor. The rapidly changing polarity of the supply would result in the motor simply going to-and-fro. S2 is the forward/reverse switch, and this is simply a d.p.d.t. switch wired so that it controls the polarity of the output signal.

The circuit of Figure 1.2 is similar to that of Figure 1.1, but T1 has a centre tap which is used as the 0 volt output of the controller. The bridge rectifier provides outputs that are about 15 volts positive and negative of the 0 volt output. VR1 enables the output potential to be varied from +15 volts down to zero, and then on to -15 volts. It therefore acts as a combined speed and direction control.

Performance

Using a potentiometer to provide speed control is simple and inexpensive, but it provides a relatively poor level of performance. There are two problems, which are poor starting performance, and inadequate speed regulation.

The speed regulation is poor due to the fact that the electric motor in the train tries to draw a much higher supply current

4

when the loading on it is increased, such as when the train climbs a gradient. The reduced resistance of the motor does give some increase in the drive current, but the motor only provides part of the load on across the d.c. supply. The rest of the load is provided by the speed control potentiometer. This limits the effect the motor can exert over the controller's output current. There is a further problem, which is that the reduced resistance through the motor results in its share of the output voltage being reduced. Thus, although more drive current is provided, the increase in the power fed to the motor changes very little. Remember that power is equal to voltage multiplied by current.

The practical result of all this is that the train has very poor speed regulation when it is run at low speeds, and the potentiometer is providing a high resistance. The train tends to stall when climbing the slightest of gradients, and it also tends to run faster when going down gradients. When going down a gradient the motor tries to draw less power, but the current only decreases slightly, and the voltage across the motor actually increases somewhat.

Simple train controllers suffer from the so called "jump start" problem. This is where the train stubbornly refuses to move until the speed control has been well advanced. In some cases it has to be taken well beyond the half speed setting before the train starts to move. Of course, once the train does start to move away, it almost instantly jumps to the relatively high speed set on the controller. Instead of gradually accelerating away, the train suddenly jumps to half speed or more, giving very unrealistic results. Some skilful and rapid adjustment of the speed control can give better results, with the speed being backed-off as soon as the train starts to move, but this is not really a satisfactory way of handling things, and always gives something less than ideal results.

"Jump starting" is primarily caused by the motor having a much lower resistance when stationary than when it is turning-over. This results in a very low voltage across the motor (and hence little drive power) until it starts to move. Less current flows through the motor once it has started, but there is a much higher voltage across it, probably giving increased power to the motor. Added to this, there is the problem of anything

5

mechanical tending to have a reluctance to start up, due to inertia, etc.

Constant Voltage

A constant voltage controller is the most simple type that is likely to provide good results. The "constant voltage" name is perhaps a bit misleading, since this type of controller provides a variable output voltage. The voltage is constant in the sense that once an output potential has been set, the output voltage remains at that level regardless of any normal changes in the loading on the controller. In practice there may actually be some variation in the output voltage with changes in loading, and this depends on the quality of the regulator used. However, any changes are relatively small, and would normally be well under one volt with the output current varied from zero to maximum.

The reason for the relatively high level of performance of a constant voltage controller is very simple. If the train starts to climb a gradient and tries to draw increased current, it is able to do so. As there is no significant series resistance to "water down" the effect of the motor's reduced resistance, the motor's drop in resistance will be fully matched by an increase in the drive current. Of equal importance, the rise in current is not counteracted by any decrease in the drive voltage, due to the regulation provided by the controller.

Starting performance is also improved. The low resistance of the stationary motor results in it drawing a heavy current initially. Even though the drive voltage is quite low, the controller is well able to supply this current. The motor draws less current once it is "up and running", but there is no sudden rise in the drive voltage as the motor's resistance rises. This gives decreased power to the motor once it has started, which helps to counteract the "jump start" effect. Unfortunately, starting performance is still less than perfect due to the mechanical characteristics of the motor, which provide the motor with a definite reluctance to start-up. With skill though, it is possible to obtain quite realistic starting, which is something that is not usually possible with the more simple types of controller.

Constant Voltage Circuit

Figure 1.3 shows the circuit diagram for the constant voltage model train controller. VR1 provides an output voltage at its wiper terminal that can be varied from zero to about 13 volts or so, but the maximum output current available from VR1 is only about one milliamp. The purpose of IC1 and TR1 is to act as a high gain buffer amplifier to enable the circuit to provide the high output currents of up to about one amp that are required in this application. IC1 is simply used as a non-inverting buffer amplifier, with TR1 connected to act as an emitter follower output stage.

TR1 is actually a power Darlington device, and its current gain is very high. In fact its current gain is typically about 5000 at high currents. It is TR1 that provides most of the circuit's current gain. Due to the fact that the output of IC1 can not swing fully positive, and there is a voltage drop of a volt or two through TR1, the maximum output voltage will be slightly less than the 13.5 volts or thereabouts at the wiper of VR1. However, the maximum output potential should still be a steady 12 volts or so, which is sufficient for this application.

C1 simply provides supply decoupling, and S1 is the forward/reverse switch. D1 suppresses any high reverse voltage spikes that might otherwise be generated across the highly inductive load provided by a small d.c. electric motor. R3 is simply a load resistor for TR1, and this ensures that the circuit works normally when no load is connected across the output. C2 prevents slight instability which otherwise causes problems, particularly at low output voltages. The current consumption of the circuit is only about 2 milliamps with zero output voltage, but this rises to as much as one amp with the train at full speed.

Mains PSU

Due to the relatively high supply voltage and maximum current consumption of the circuit, a mains power supply unit is the only realistic means of powering it. The circuit requires a reasonably stable and well smoothed supply of about 15 to 18 volts. Figure 1.4 shows the circuit diagram for a suitable 15 volt mains power supply unit (PSU).

This circuit is a conventional type having S1 to provide on/off switching, and mains transformer T1 to provide the

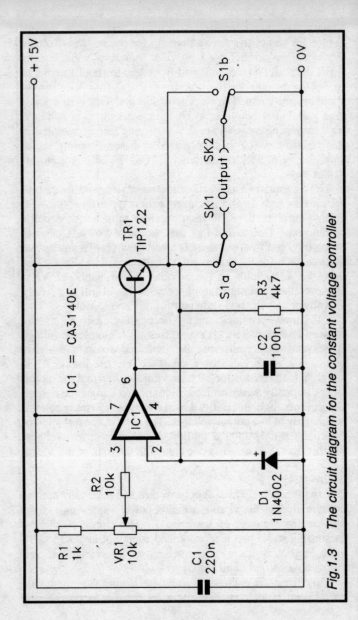

Fig.1.3   The circuit diagram for the constant voltage controller

8

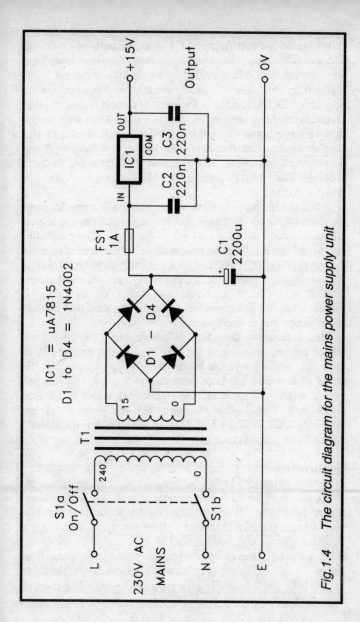

Fig.1.4   The circuit diagram for the mains power supply unit

IC1 = uA7815
D1 to D4 = 1N4002

9

necessary voltage step-down and isolation. D1 to D4 form a full-wave bridge rectifier, and C1 is the smoothing capacitor. FS1 provides protection against medium term overloads, but the main protection is provided by the fold-back current limiting in IC1. This almost instantly reduces the output current to only about 230 milliamps in the event of a short circuit or other severe overload on the output. IC1 is a 15 volt one amp monolithic voltage regulator, and it provides a well smoothed and regulated output to the controller circuit. C2 and C3 are decoupling components which ensure IC1 does not become unstable. They must be fitted close to IC1, where they can have maximum effect.

A maximum output current of one amp is sufficient for most locomotives up to 00 gauge, but larger gauges require higher output currents, as do a few 00 gauge types. The controller circuit of Figure 1.3 can be used with an output current of up to 2 amps provided TR1 is fitted with a suitably large heatsink, but the mains power supply circuit obviously requires some modification in order to accommodate higher supply currents. Figure 1.5 shows the circuit diagram for the modified version of the mains power supply circuit.

This is basically the same as before, but T1 must have a higher current rating, and the rectifiers in the bridge circuit have also been changed to higher current types. Similarly, the rating of fuse FS1 has been increased to 2 amps, and IC1 has been changed to a uA78S15 (or equivalent), which is a 2 amp regulator. The only other change is that the value of C1 has been increased, so that a high level of smoothing is maintained at maximum output current.

Construction

A suitable stripboard layout for the constant voltage controller is shown in Figure 1.6 (component layout and wiring), and Figure 1.7 (underside view). The board is a standard 0.1 inch pitch type, and it has 20 holes by 19 copper strips. This is not a standard size in which the board is sold, and a board of the correct size must therefore be trimmed from a larger piece. The board is easily cut using a hacksaw or junior hacksaw, but there is very little space between adjacent holes, so cut along rows of holes and not between them. This leaves rather rough sawn

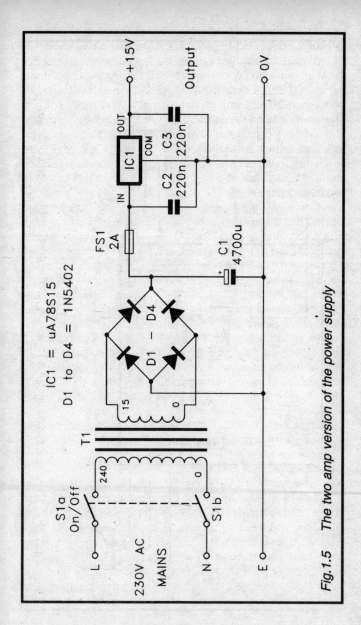

Fig.1.5 The two amp version of the power supply

11

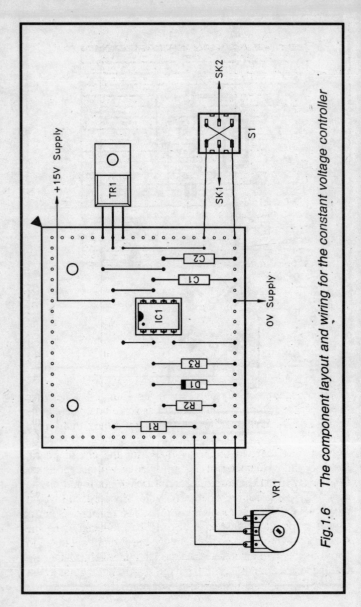

Fig.1.6   The component layout and wiring for the constant voltage controller

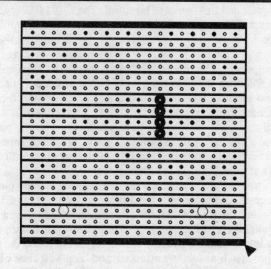

*Fig.1.7   The underside of the constant voltage
controller board*

edges, but they are easily smoothed using a small flat file. Take
due care when working on stripboard as some boards are quite
brittle, and are likely to snap or even shatter if they are handled
roughly.

Next drill the two mounting holes for the circuit board.
Holes having a diameter of 3.3 millimetres will accept either
6BA or metric M3 screws. In general I have not found plastic
stand-offs very effective when used with stripboard, so I would
recommend the use of mounting screws. The four breaks in the
copper strips are made next. They can be produced using the
special cutting tool, or a hand-held twist drill bit of about 4.5 to
5 millimetres in diameter will do the job quite well. Make sure
that the strips are cut across their full width, but try not to cut
so deep that the board is seriously weakened.

13

The board is then ready for the components, single-sided solder pins, and link-wires to be added. The CA3140E used for IC1 has a PMOS input stage which renders it vulnerable to damage by static charges. Accordingly, the normal anti-static handling precautions should be observed when dealing with this component. The most important of these is to use a holder, so that soldering direct to the pins of IC1 is avoided. Do not fit IC1 into its holder until the board and all the point-to-point wiring have been completed. It should be supplied in some form of anti-static packing, such as conductive foam, a plastic tube, or a special form of "blister" pack. Whatever form the anti-static packing takes, leave IC1 in the packing until it is time for it to be plugged into the holder.

Constructors are sometimes advised not to touch the pins of static-sensitive components, but this is not really very practical. As supplied, the pins of d.i.l. integrated circuits are splayed outwards slightly, and they must be pinched inwards before they will fit into a holder correctly. However, do not touch the pins any more than is absolutely essential, and keep well clear of any obvious sources of static electricity when handling IC1, or any other static-sensitive components. Potential sources of static electricity include television sets and computer monitors, as well as the traditional culprits such carpets and clothes made from man-made fibres, and some pets such as cats.

The other components are less problematic, but be careful to get D1 fitted the right way round. It will virtually short-circuit the output of the controller if it is fitted with the wrong polarity. The link-wires are made from either 22 or 24 s.w.g. tinned copper wire. My preference is the slightly thicker gauge (22 s.w.g.), but both thicknesses will do the job perfectly well.

Heatsink

TR1 is shown in Fig.1.6 as being fitted direct onto the board, but it might be necessary to mount it off-board and hard wire it to the appropriate three points on the board via solder-pins. The reason for this is that TR1 has to dissipate several watts when the controller is set at medium to high output voltages. Unless TR1 is fitted on a suitably large heatsink, in use it will rapidly overheat and be destroyed. For a one amp version of the controller one of the larger bolt-on heatsinks having a rating of

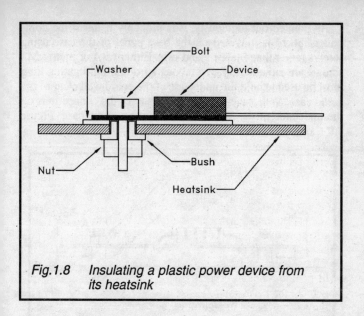

Fig.1.8   Insulating a plastic power device from its heatsink

about nine degrees celsius per watt should just about suffice. However, it would be safer to use a larger type. For a two amp version of the unit a heatsink having a rating of about four degrees celsius per watt is required. The unit should be housed in a metal case, and there should be no difficulty in using this as the heatsink. TR1 can be mounted direct onto the case, but things are likely to be more satisfactory if it is mounted on the rear panel via a simple "L"-shaped bracket fabricated from 16 or 18 s.w.g. aluminium.

The collector terminal of TR1 connects internally to its heat-tab, and this means that in most cases it will be essential to insulate TR1 from the heatsink. A suitable insulating kit containing a thin mica washer and a plastic insulating bush is available from most electronic component retailers. The mica washer is placed between TR1 and the heatsink to provide the main insulation, and the plastic bush is used to ensure that the mounting screw does not provide a path of conduction between the heat-tab and the heatsink. Figure 1.8 shows the way in which the washer and bush are used.

As pointed out previously, it is probably better if the component board is mounted on the base panel of the case using screws rather than plastic stand-offs. Either 6BA or metric M3 screws are suitable. Spacers about 10 or 12 millimetres long must be used to hold the underside of the board well clear of the metal case, so that there is no risk of any of the connections on the underside of the board short circuiting to the case. Figure 1.9 shows this general scheme of things.

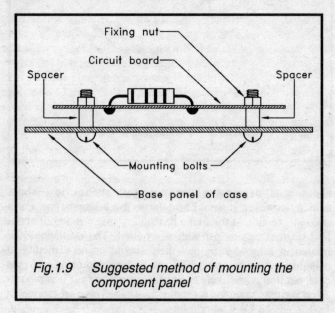

Fig.1.9   *Suggested method of mounting the component panel*

VR1 and S1 are mounted on the front panel. Most potentiometers require 10 millimetre diameter mounting holes, but there are miniature types which require smaller mounting holes. The component retailer's catalogue should state the correct size for the mounting hole, or you can simply measure it using a ruler. Most miniature toggle switches require a 6.35 millimetre hole in the front panel, but again, it is as well to check the retailer's catalogue or to actually measure the diameter of the component's mounting bush. Accurate control of the train's speed will be easier if VR1 is fitted with a large control knob.

To complete the controller, add the point-to-point wiring. Use ordinary 7/0.2 multi-strand, p.v.c. insulated connecting wire. Tin all the component tags and the tops of the solder-pins with plenty of solder, and also tin the end ends of each lead prior to fitting it into place. There should then be no difficulty in making strong and reliable soldered joints.

PSU Construction

It is assumed here that the mains power supply unit will be built as a separate unit, connected to the controller via a twin lead and suitable plugs and sockets (such as four millimetre "wander" plugs and sockets). Of course, if preferred the power supply and controller can be built as a single unit, and this is in many ways a much more satisfactory way of doing things. The only real advantage of having a separate power supply is that it makes life easier if you wish to experiment with different controllers.

Whether the power supply is built as a separate unit, or integrated with the controller, it should only be constructed by those who have a reasonable amount of experience at electronic project construction. Mains powered projects are not a suitable starting point for beginners. The mains supply is very dangerous, and mistakes could easily prove to be fatal. Those who lack the necessary experience and expertise should power the controller circuits featured in this book from a ready-made power supply capable of providing 15 volts at one or two amps (as appropriate for your layout).

Figure 1.10 shows the stripboard layout and wiring for the mains power supply. The underside view of the component panel is provided in Figure 1.11. The board has 24 holes by 24 copper strips. This component layout was designed with a one amp version of the supply in mind, but provided C1 is a modern and reasonably small type, it will just about suffice for a two amp version of the supply.

Construction of the stripboard follows along the same lines as construction of the controller board, but extra care should be taken in this case. In particular, make quite sure that C1 and the four rectifiers are fitted the right way round. Mistakes here could result in costly damage, and could even be dangerous.

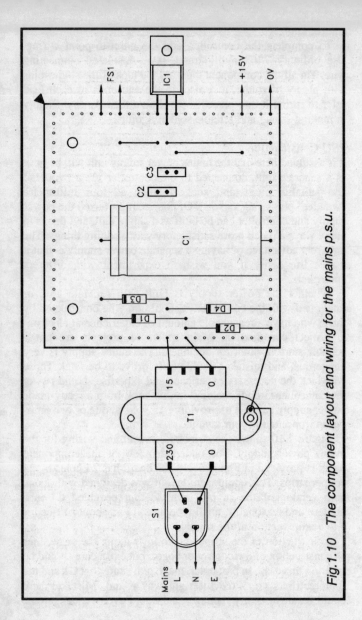

Fig.1.10 The component layout and wiring for the mains p.s.u.

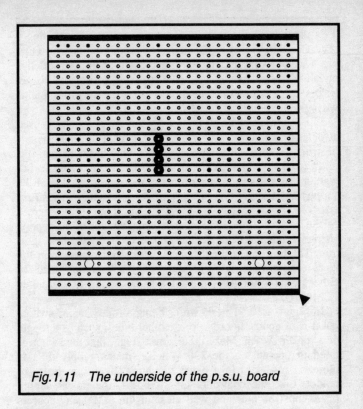

Fig.1.11 The underside of the p.s.u. board

For similar reasons, make quite sure that the breaks in the copper strips are all present and correct.

There are actually one or two breaks in the strips that are not strictly necessary, but they reduce the risk of unwanted connections between the input and output sections of the circuit due accidental short circuits between adjacent copper strips. These occur quite easily when using stripboard, where it is easy to bridge strips by applying slightly too much solder to a joint. You certainly need to be on your guard against problems with excess solder, and if a stripboard based project fails to work I always check for this problem first.

For reasons of safety it is essential for a mains powered project such as this to be housed in an a metal case which must be earthed to the mains earth lead. A soldertag fitted on one of T1's mounting bolts represents an easy means of providing a secure earthing point on the case. The case must be a type that has a screw fixing lid, and not one that has some form of clip-on lid or cover that would make it easy for someone to get access to, and possibly touch, part of the dangerous mains wiring.

IC1 has to dissipate a few watts when the controller is used at or near full speed. Accordingly, IC1 must be fitted with a heatsink to prevent it from overheating. One of the larger bolt-on heatsinks having a rating of about nine degrees celsius per watt or less will just about suffice for a one amp version of the supply, but a larger type gives a more satisfactory margin for error. A heatsink having a rating of about four degrees celsius per watt is required for a two amp version of the supply. Using the metal case as the heatsink is probably the best solution. The heat-tab will either be electrically isolated from the three leadout wires, or it will connect to the "common" lead. In either case it is not necessary to use an insulation kit to insulate IC1 from the case.

In Figure 1.10 S1 is shown as being a rotary mains switch, but it is of course in order to use other types, such as a toggle or a rocker switch. Make quite sure though, that the switch is rated to operate on the 230 volt a.c. mains supply. FS1 is mounted off-board in a panel mounting 20 millimetre fuse-holder. Like the controller circuit board, the power supply board must be mounted well clear of the case using spacers about 10 or 12 millimetres long. The hard wiring is very simple and straightforward, but take extra care here as some of the wiring connects direct to the mains supply. Double check the circuit board and all the wiring before testing the power supply.

In Use

If you have access to a multi-range test meter it is a good idea to check the output voltage from the power supply circuit to ensure that it is within a few percent of the correct figure of 15 volts. The multimeter can then be used to check that the controller provides an output voltage that can be varied by means of VR1 from 0 volts (fully counter-clockwise) to about 12 volts (fully clockwise). If all is well, or you do not have access to test equipment, try out the controller in earnest.

There will be a range of low settings on VR1 that do not cause the train to move. This is simply because a few volts are needed before the motor is fed with sufficient power to move the train. The setting on VR1 that causes the train to move off varies considerably from one train to another. Once under way, VR1 should enable the speed of the train to be varied smoothly, making it easy to set any desired speed.

Components for Figure 1.3

Resistors (all 0.25 watt 5% carbon film)
R1   1k
R2   10k
R3   4k7

Capacitors
C1   220n ceramic
C2   100n ceramic

Potentiometer
VR1   10k lin carbon

Semiconductors
IC1   CA3140E
D1   1N4002
TR1   TIP122 or TIP121

Miscellaneous
S1   d.p.d.t. miniature toggle switch
SK1   4mm socket
SK2   4mm socket

Metal instrument case, 0.1 inch pitch stripboard having 20 holes by 19 copper strips, 8-pin d.i.l. holder, large control knob, multi-strand connecting wire, single-sided solder pins, solder, etc.

Components for Figure 1.4

Capacitors
C1   2200μ 25V axial electrolytic
C2   220n ceramic
C3   220n ceramic

Semiconductors

IC1	µA7815 (1A 15V positive regulator)
D1	1N4002
D2	1N4002
D3	1N4002
D4	1N4002

Miscellaneous

T1	Standard mains primary, 15 volt 2 amp secondary
FS1	1A 20mm quick-blow fuse
S1	Rotary mains switch

Metal instrument case, 0.1 inch pitch stripboard having 24 holes by 24 copper strips, 20mm panel mounting fuse-holder, multi-strand connecting wire, mains plug (fitted with 2A or 3A fuse) and lead, single-sided solder pins, solder, etc.

Components for Figure 1.5

Capacitors

C1	4700µ 25V axial electrolytic
C2	220n ceramic
C3	220n ceramic

Semiconductors

IC1	µA78S15 (2A 15V positive regulator)
D1	1N5402
D2	1N5402
D3	1N5402
D4	1N5402

Miscellaneous

FS1	2A 20mm quick-blow fuse
S1	Rotary mains switch

Metal instrument case, 0.1 inch pitch stripboard having 24 holes by 24 copper strips, 20mm panel mounting fuse-holder, multi-strand connecting wire, mains plug (fitted with 2A or 3A fuse) and lead, single-sided solder pins, solder, etc.

Pulse Control

A constant voltage controller provides much better control of the train than a simple potentiometer type, but performance still falls some way short of perfection. There are two main approaches to obtaining even better performance, and one of these is to use what is, in effect, an overcompensated voltage regulator. In other words, when the motor increases the loading on the supply, a normal voltage regulator simply maintains the output voltage at a more or less constant voltage. An over-compensated circuit actually produces a higher output voltage when the loading is increased, and a lower voltage when it is decreased.

In practice I have found it difficult to get consistently good results with this type of circuit. The problem is that the control characteristic of the controller must be accurately matched to the characteristics of the motor. Any mismatch produces a lack of speed stability, possibly with the train actually going faster up gradients, and stalling on the way down them.

I have always found the alternative of pulse control to be a better choice where the motor being driven is something of "an unknown quantity." The principle of pulse control is quite simple to understand, and it relies on the fact that a small d.c. electric motor will work perfectly well if it is driven by a series of pulses rather than by a steady voltage. The pulse frequency must not be too low, which in practice usually means no less than about 50Hz. Lower frequencies tend to drive the motor in short bursts rather than giving something approximating to continuous operation. High pulse frequencies are not usable as the motor has a high impedance at these frequencies, and the current flow is too small to drive the motor properly. Frequencies of up to a few kilohertz are often quite acceptable, but a frequency of no more than a few hundred hertz is safer.

Pulse control relies on the fact that the average voltage of a pulse signal can be varied by altering its mark-space ratio. Consider the three waveforms show in Figure 1.12. The mark-space ratio of waveform (a) is quite high, and is actually 1 : 7. The signal is therefore high for one eighth of the time, and the average output voltage is therefore one eighth of the supply voltage (as indicated by the broken line). In waveform (b) the pulse length has been doubled, but the frequency is unchanged,

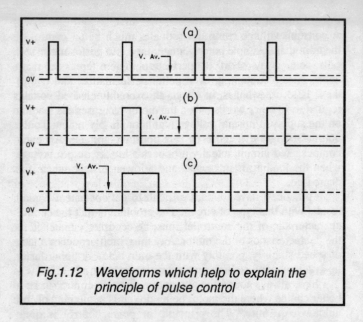

Fig.1.12 Waveforms which help to explain the
principle of pulse control

giving a mark-space ratio of 1 : 3, and an average output voltage that is one quarter of the supply potential. In waveform (c) there is a further doubling of the pulse length, and the output frequency has again been kept unchanged. This gives a 1 : 1 mark-space ratio, and an average output voltage that is half the supply potential. If things were taken a stage further and the pulse length was doubled again, the output would be high all the time, and the average output voltage would obviously be equal to the supply voltage.

Clearly it is possible to obtain any desired average output voltage using the pulse method of control, but on the face of it there is no advantage in using this method of control. An important point to bear in mind here is that the problem of poor speed regulation and stalling occurs when trains are travelling slowly. The motor is then producing very little power, and external influences can easily affect the motor's speed, or even halt it altogether. With the pulse method of control, at low speeds the motor is driven intermittently at full power. These bursts at full power resist changes in speed, and stalling. Even if the train

24

should stall, it is quite likely that the bursts of full power will almost instantly nudge it into action again.

In practice pulse controllers certainly give excellent results, and permit very realistic results to be obtained. Trains can slowly accelerate away, and be brought to a standstill equally gradually. Provided the tracks are kept reasonably clean, the trains can also be run at very slow speeds for long periods of time without the train continually grinding to a halt. However, pulse controllers are not without one or two foibles. One potential problem is that the pulsed nature of the signal can result in the tracks radiating radio frequency interference. In practice this does not seem to be a major problem, and the low frequency of the signal means that it is not essential for the signal to contain high frequencies in order to provide a wide range of speeds.

Another problem is simply that the pulsing of the motor tends to result in it "humming" at the output frequency of the controller. Unfortunately, there is no way around this problem, and a certain amount of "humming" and "buzzing" just has to be tolerated when using this type of controller. It is difficult to regard this as a major drawback though, and small d.c. electric motors produce a fair amount of "humming" and "buzzing" sounds regardless of the control method.

Some model railway enthusiasts feel that pulsed controllers are more prone to problems with motors being accidentally burnt out. However, there is no obvious reason why this should be any more of a problem with pulsed controllers than with any other type. All the controller circuits in this book are designed for use with a current limited mains power supply, and the overload protection in the power supply should protect the motor as well as the controller circuit. I have certainly had no problems with pulsed controllers causing any damage to locomotives.

Pulse Controller Circuit

A pulse controller circuit can be very simple indeed, and the one featured here (Figure 1.13) only uses a handful of components. The circuit is based on the familiar 555 timer integrated circuit (IC1) which is used in a slightly modified version of the astable (oscillator) mode. Figure 1.14 shows the basic circuit for a 555 astable. The basic action of the circuit is for timing capacitor C1 to first be charged to two thirds of the

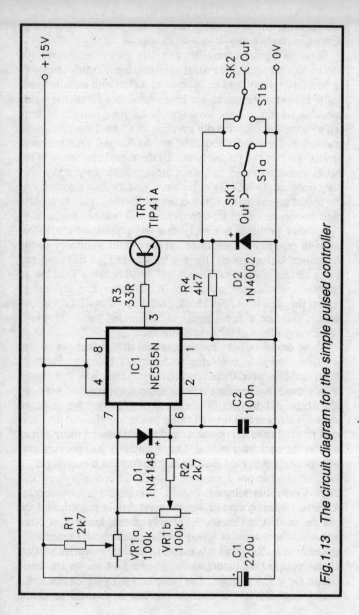

Fig.1.13   The circuit diagram for the simple pulsed controller

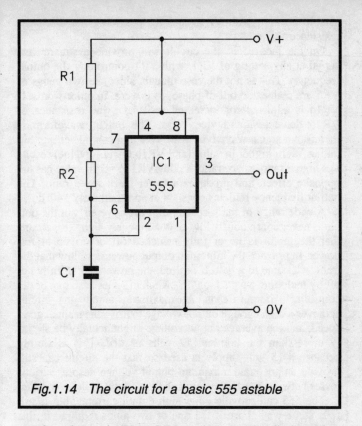

Fig.1.14 The circuit for a basic 555 astable

supply voltage via R1 and R2, and to then be discharged to one-third of the supply potential via R2 and an internal switching transistor of the 555. This action continues indefinitely, with the output at pin 3 going high while C1 is being charged, and low while it is being discharged. This results in a rectangular output signal being produced at pin 3.

In this circuit the mark-space ratio of the output signal is made variable by using variable resistances for both sections of the timing resistance, and by the inclusion of steering diode D1. D1 effectively short circuits VR1b and R2 during the charge cycle, leaving R1 and VR1a as the charge resistance. During the discharge cycle the circuit operates in the normal 555 astable fashion, with VR1b and R2 providing the discharge resistance.

On the face of it, the circuit will provide a squarewave signal at any setting of VR1, with VR1 controlling the output frequency. This is not the case though, since the two gangs of VR1 are connected out-of-phase, as it were. In other words, if VR1a is adjusted for increased resistance, the resistance of VR1b decreases, and vice versa. The output waveform is therefore a squarewave type with VR1 at a central setting, but taking VR1a higher in value (and VR1b lower in value) results in a higher mark-space ratio. Taking VR1 lower in value has the opposite effect, and produces a lower mark-space ratio. The output frequency remains constant at approximately 140Hz.

A wide range of mark-space ratios are covered, but the output is never continuously low, or continuously high. This means that the motor is never fully switched off or driven at full power. In practice the minimum output power is so low that the train will come to a halt. If desired, the power can be fully cut off by including a s.p.s.t. on/off switch in series with one of the controller's output leads. At maximum output the circuit achieves a high enough output voltage to drive the train at good speed, and the average output voltage might actually be slightly more than the nominal 12 volts needed. This is simply because a 15 volt supply is used so that the circuit can still provide an adequate maximum output voltage despite various losses between the supply input and the output of the controller.

The 555 can provide quite high output currents, but it still falls some way short of the one or two amps required in this application. TR1 is therefore used as an emitter follower buffer stage at the output of IC1, and this enables the circuit to comfortably handle the required output currents. My original circuit had a major problem with high frequency instability, and this produced erratic operation. R3 is "base stopper" resistor which completely eliminates the instability. R4 is the load resistor for TR1, and D2 is a protection diode. S1 is the usual forward/reverse switch.

Construction

The stripboard component layout and hard wiring are shown in Figure 1.15, and the underside view of the board is provided in

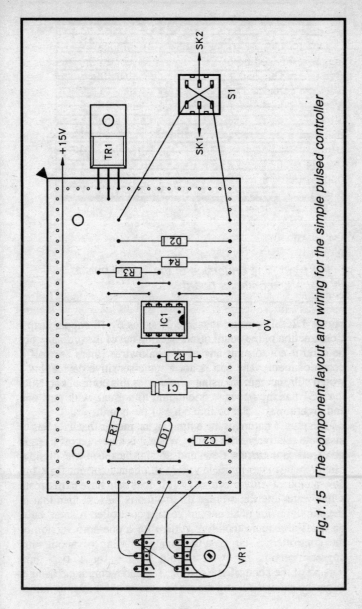

Fig.1.15   The component layout and wiring for the simple pulsed controller

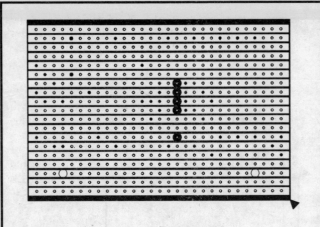

Fig.1.16   The underside of the simple pulsed controller board

Figure 1.16. The board measure 29 holes by 18 copper strips. Construction of the board offers nothing out of the ordinary, but be careful not to omit any of the link-wires (there are half a dozen of them). The 555 is not a static-sensitive device, but I would still recommend using a holder for this component. Note that IC1 has the opposite orientation to normal, with pins one and eight towards the bottom edge of the board.

The pulsed nature of the output signal means that TR1 has to dissipate relatively little power. When it is switched off there is no significant current flow, and no significant power dissipation. When it is switched on there is a heavy current flow, but only a modest voltage across TR1. It does then have to dissipate a few watts, but the average dissipation is far less than that in the output device in a constant voltage controller. A small bolt-on heatsink should therefore suffice for a one amp version of the controller. A larger type having a rating of about nine degrees celsius per watt should suffice for a two amp version of the controller. However, I would recommend using a larger heatsink, or using the metal case as the heatsink, rather

30

than risking the bare minimum of heatsinking. Bear in mind that the heat-tab of TR1 connects internally to its collector terminal, and where appropriate use an insulation kit to insulate it from the heatsink.

In Use

Like the constant voltage controller, this pulsed controller will have a small range of low speed settings that do not result in the train moving. Again, the width of this range is dependent on a number of factors, including the exact characteristics of the electric motor. The rest of VR1's adjustment range should provide smooth and accurate control of the train's speed. It should also be possible to gradually accelerate the train away from a standing start, obtaining good realism. It should also be possible to have the train run at very low speeds without any stalling problems, but this is dependent on the tracks and the pick-up wheels of the train being in good and clean condition. If the motor loses electrical contact with the track, the train will stop, regardless of how good or bad the controller happens to be.

Due to the pulsed nature of the controller's output signal there will be a certain amount of "hum" from the electric motor. If this seems to be excessive it is possible that the output frequency of the controller is coinciding with a mechanical resonance of the motor, or perhaps something in the structure of the locomotive itself is resonating. Making C2 a little higher or lower in value will alter the controller's output frequency, and should eliminate any problem with mechanical resonance.

Components – Figure 1.13

Resistors (all 0.25 watt 5% carbon film)

R1	2k7
R2	2k7
R3	33R
R4	4k7

Potentiometer

VR1	100k dual gang lin

Capacitors
C1   220µ 16V axial elect
C2   100n polyester

Semiconductors
IC1   NE555N
D1   1N4148
D2   1N4002

Miscellaneous
S1   d.p.d.t. miniature toggle switch
SK1   4mm socket
SK2   4mm socket

Metal instrument case, 0.1 inch pitch stripboard having 29 holes by 18 copper strips, 8-pin d.i.l. holder, large control knob, multi-strand connecting wire, single-sided solder pins, solder, etc.

"Improved" Pulsed Controller

This "improved" pulsed controller provides a slightly greater control range, so that power to the train can be varied from absolutely zero to a continuous 12 volts or so. Of more importance, it is controlled via a voltage rather than varying resistances. This makes it possible to have a more sophisticated controller which provides simulated inertia, momentum, and braking. The circuit is based on a conventional pulse width modulator. Figure 1.17 shows the block diagram for the controller. The clock oscillator and voltage comparator stages form the pulse width modulator, and the buffer amplifier simply enables the circuit to provide the relatively high output currents required in this application.

The voltage comparator has one input (usually the non-inverting input) fed with the input voltage, and the other input fed from the clock oscillator. It is essential to the operation of the circuit that the clock signal is a reasonably good triangular type. In an application of this type a high degree of linearity through the system is not really needed, so a few imperfections in the clock signal are tolerable.

With zero input voltage the clock signal will always be at the higher potential, and the output of the comparator will always

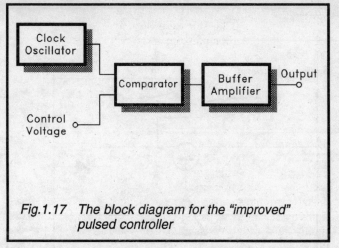

Fig.1.17 The block diagram for the "improved" pulsed controller

be low. A small input voltage will result in the clock signal being at the higher voltage for the majority of the time. The output of the comparator is therefore pulsed at the clock frequency, but will be low for the majority of the time, giving a low average output voltage. If the input voltage is increased, the clock signal will be higher than the input voltage for a lesser proportion of the time. This gives a higher average output voltage. If the output voltage of the converter is taken high enough, it will always be higher than the clock voltage, and the output of the comparator will go high continuously.

In this case there is a slight problem in that we require the full output range to be covered with an input voltage range of zero to a higher voltage of around 5 to 12 volts. It is difficult to produce a clock oscillator that provides a suitable signal. The circuit is therefore based on a fairly conventional clock oscillator, and a simple level shifter circuit is then used to drop the voltages in the output signal to a suitable range.

The Circuit
The circuit diagram for the p.w.m. controller appears in Figure 1.18. This is the basic version having a conventional speed control. Other versions of the unit which include simulated inertia, momentum, and braking are described later in this chapter.

33

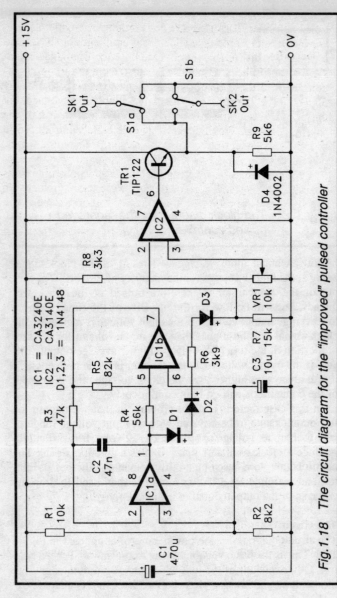

Fig.1.18 The circuit diagram for the "improved" pulsed controller

34

The clock oscillator is based on IC1, which is a dual operational amplifier. It is used in a conventional triangular/square-wave oscillator of the type which uses an integrator (IC1a) and a trigger circuit (IC1b). In this case only the triangular output signal from IC1a is required. C2 and R3 are the timing components, and these set the clock frequency at approximately 350Hz. R1, R2, and C3 provide a mid-supply bias voltage, but the actual bias voltage is actually a little less than half the supply potential. This imbalance is deliberately introduced in order to counteract the lack of symmetry in IC1's output stages, and it results in a more symmetrical clock signal.

IC1a's output signal has an amplitude of about nine volts peak-to-peak, and even allowing for the lack of symmetry in the biasing, its minimum voltage is still well above the 0 volt rail. A small amount of attenuation is introduced by R6 and R7, but on its own this is not enough to give the desired effect. The main voltage drop is provided by D1 to D3, which are silicon diodes that are always forward biased. They introduce a voltage drop of almost two volts, which takes the minimum clock voltage down to an acceptable level.

IC2 is an operational amplifier, but in this circuit it functions as the voltage comparator. TR1 is the output buffer stage, and it is a power Darlington device used in the emitter follower mode. R9 acts as its load resistance with no external load connected across the output. D4 suppresses any reverse voltage spikes generated across the highly inductive loading provided by a d.c. electric motor.

Construction

Figures 1.19 and 1.20 respectively show the component layout and underside views for the "improved" pulsed controller. The stripboard panel has 39 holes by 21 copper strips. Construction of the component panel follows along the normal lines, but remember that both integrated circuits are static-sensitive. Like TR1 in the simple pulsed controller described previously, TR1 in this circuit must, as a bare minimum, be fitted with a bolt-on heatsink.

This controller should give good performance with smooth start-ups and stall-free operation at low speeds. At minimum output the power should be totally cut off, giving no "hum" at

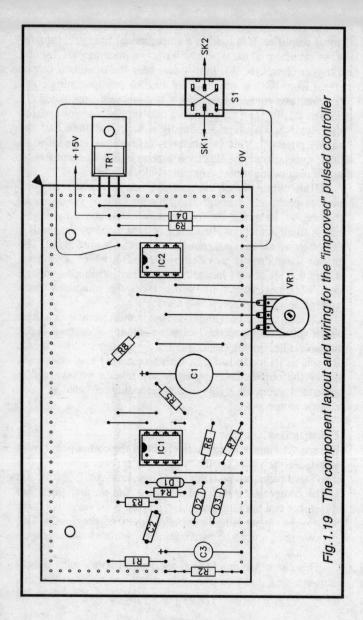

Fig.1.19 The component layout and wiring for the "improved" pulsed controller

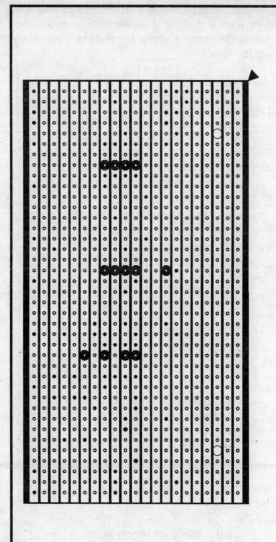

Fig.1.20 The underside of the "improved" pulsed controller board

37

all from the locomotive. If problems with resonances are experienced when the train is running at low to medium speeds, try altering the clock frequency slightly by making C2 slightly higher or lower in value.

Components for Figure 1.18

Resistors (all 0.25 watt 5% carbon film)
R1	10k
R2	8k2
R3	47k
R4	56k
R5	82k
R6	3k9
R7	15k
R8	3k3
R9	5k6

Potentiometer
VR1	10k lin carbon

Capacitors
C1	470µ 16V radial elect
C2	47n polyester
C3	10µ 25V radial elect

Semiconductors
IC1	CA3240E
IC2	CA3140E
D1	1N4148
D2	1N4148
D3	1N4148
D4	1N4002
TR1	TIP122 or TIP121

Miscellaneous
S1	d.p.d.t. miniature toggle switch
SK1	4mm socket
SK2	4mm socket

Metal instrument case, 0.1 inch pitch stripboard having 39

holes by 21 copper strips, 8-pin d.i.l. holder (2 off), large control knob, multi-strand connecting wire, single-sided solder pins, solder, etc.

Pushbutton Control

The basic controller circuit of Figure 1.18 is easily modified to provide alternative methods of control, including computer control. This is a topic that is covered in chapter 3, which covers the general subject of using personal computers to control model railways. To complete this chapter we will consider two interesting methods of manual control, and the first of these is pushbutton control. This requires rather more skill than "driving" the train via a simple speed control, and in my opinion at any rate, it provides a lot more fun than a simple speed control.

This version of the controller has three pushbutton switches which act as the throttle, brake, and stop controls. The latter is not operated in normal use, and is really included as a quick means of cutting off power to the tracks if things go wrong. The train is normally "driven" by first holding down the "throttle" button, which slowly accelerates the train. The "throttle" button is released as soon as the train has reached the desired speed. The train then coasts, and will gradually come to a halt unless the "throttle" control is pressed periodically. The train is brought to a halt by pressing the "brake" button. This gives much less abrupt deceleration than the "stop" control, but it still takes the train a few seconds to come to a halt.

The Circuit

The circuit diagram for the pushbutton controller is shown in Figures 1.21 and 1.22. The main circuit is shown in Figure 1.21, and this is essentially the same as the "improved" pulse controller circuit, but the speed control potentiometer has been omitted. Instead, the control voltage is provided by the circuit of Figure 1.22. This is basically just a standard C – R timing circuit which has one capacitive element (C4), and four resistors to control the charging and discharging of the capacitor.

Initially there is no charge on C4, which means there is zero control voltage, and zero output from the controller. Operating

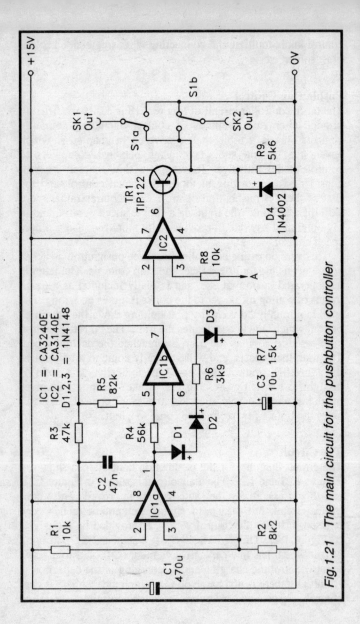

Fig.1.21   The main circuit for the pushbutton controller

40

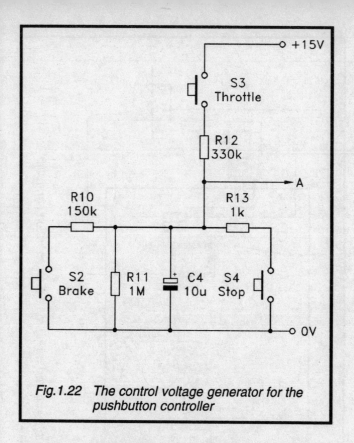

Fig.1.22 The control voltage generator for the pushbutton controller

S3 results in C4 charging from the positive supply via R12. This gives a control voltage that rises quite quickly at first, but the rate of rise steadily falls as the charge voltage on C4 gets closer to the 15 volt supply potential. In practice this seems to give a good control characteristic, with the train accelerating in a reasonably realistic fashion. When S3 is released, C4 discharges through R11, but only very slowly due to the high value of this component. This gives the gradual slowing of the train when the "throttle" is switched off. Pressing S2 adds R10 in parallel with R11, which gives a much higher discharge rate, and brings the train to a halt more rapidly. Operating S4 results

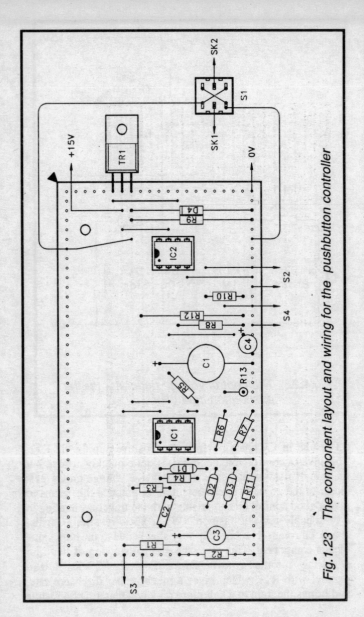

Fig.1.23 The component layout and wiring for the pushbutton controller

42

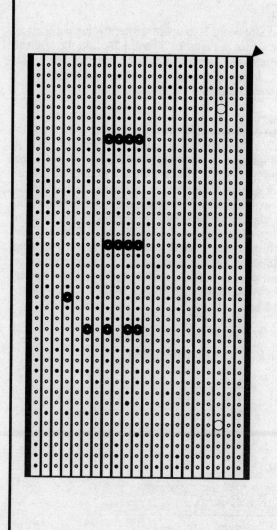

Fig. 1.24   The underside of the pushbutton controller board

in C4 discharging very rapidly through R13, and brings the
train to an abrupt halt.

Construction

The modified stripboard layout and wiring for the pushbutton
controller are shown in Figures 1.23 and 1.24. Like the original
design, these are based on a board which has 39 holes by 21
copper strips. In fact the component layout used here is just a
slightly revamped version of the original.

Customising

With this type of project each constructor tends to have his or
her own view about the rate at which the "throttle" control
should cause the train to accelerate, and the rate at which the
"brake" control should decelerate the train. Both the acceleration and deceleration times can be increased by making C4
higher in value, or decreased by making C4 lower in value. The
acceleration rate can be increased by decreasing the value of
R12, or decreased by using a higher value here. Similarly, the
rate at which the train "brakes" can be increased by making
R10 lower in value, or decreased by using a higher value for
R10. A higher value for R11 causes the train to coast for longer,
while a lower value reduces the time taken for it to slow down
and coast to a halt.

Components for Figures 1.21 and 1.22

Resistors (all 0.25 watt 5% carbon film)

R1	10k
R2	8k2
R3	47k
R4	56k
R5	82k
R6	3k9
R7	15k
R8	10k
R9	5k6
R10	150k
R11	1M
R12	330k
R13	1k

Capacitors

C1	470µ 16V radial elect
C2	47n polyester
C3	10µ 25V radial elect
C4	10µ 25V radial elect

Semiconductors

IC1	CA3240E
IC2	CA3140E
D1	1N4148
D2	1N4148
D3	1N4148
D4	1N4002
TR1	TIP122 or TIP121

Miscellaneous

S1	d.p.d.t. miniature toggle switch
S2	push-to-make pushbutton switch
S3	push-to-make pushbutton switch
S4	push-to-make pushbutton switch
SK1	4mm socket
SK2	4mm socket

Metal instrument case, 0.1 inch pitch stripboard having 39 holes by 21 copper strips, 8-pin d.i.l. holder (2 off), multi-strand connecting wire, single-sided solder pins, solder, etc.

Inertia Controller

This version of the controller has a speed control potentiometer, but it also has simulated inertia, momentum, and braking. In other words, setting a certain speed using the speed control will not result in the train almost instantly going at that speed. Instead, the train gradually accelerates to the speed set using the speed control. This is the simulated inertia. When the speed control is backed off, the simulated momentum results in the train gradually coasting to a halt. The train can be brought to a more rapid halt by applying the simulated braking.

The main circuit for the inertia controller is the same as the main circuit for the pushbutton controller (Figure 1.21). The control voltage is generated using the circuit shown in Figure 1.25. This has definite similarities to the control voltage

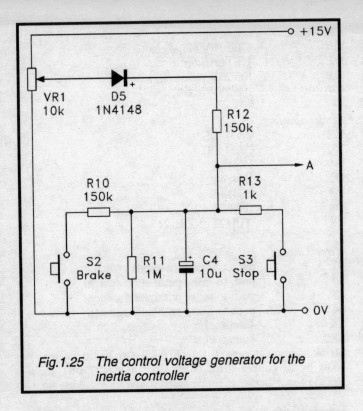

Fig.1.25   The control voltage generator for the inertia controller

generator circuit of the pushbutton controller, including the same "brake" and "stop" controls. The only difference is that the "throttle" control section has been replaced by VR1, D5, and R12. VR1 is the speed control, but the inclusion of R12 in series with its output means that any increase in the wiper voltage is not immediately matched by an increase in the output voltage. The voltage changes gradually as C4 charges via R12. D5 prevents C4 from discharging through R12 and VR1 when VR1 is backed off, and its wiper voltage is reduced. C4 can only discharge though R11, which gives a relatively slow discharge rate.

The stripboard component layout, wiring, and underside view of the board are provided in Figures 1.26 and 1.27. Once

46

again, the board has 39 holes by 21 copper strips.

Components – Figures 1.21 and 1.25

Resistors (all 0.25 watt 5% carbon film)
R1	10k
R2	8k2
R3	47k
R4	56k
R5	82k
R6	3k9
R7	15k
R8	10k
R9	5k6
R10	150k
R11	1M
R12	150k
R13	1k

Potentiometer
VR1	10k lin carbon

Capacitors
C1	470µ 16V radial elect
C2	47n polyester
C3	10µ 25V radial elect
C4	10µ 25V radial elect

Semiconductors
IC1	CA3240E
IC2	CA3140E
D1	1N4148
D2	1N4148
D3	1N4148
D4	1N4002
D5	1N4148
TR1	TIP122 or TIP121

Miscellaneous
S1	d.p.d.t. miniature toggle switch

47

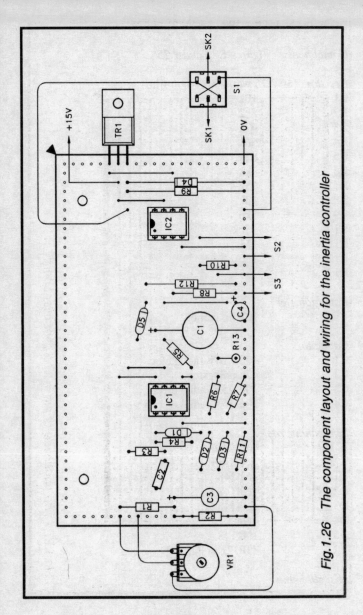

Fig.1.26   The component layout and wiring for the inertia controller

48

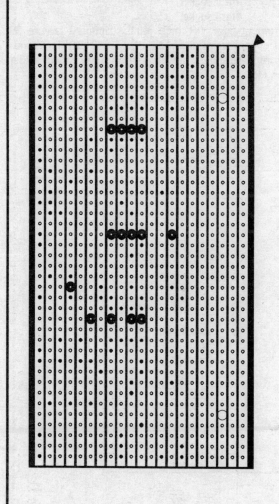

Fig.1.27 The underside of the inertia controller board

S2	push-to-make pushbutton switch
S3	push-to-make pushbutton switch
SK1	4mm socket
SK2	4mm socket

Metal instrument case, 0.1 inch pitch stripboard having 39 holes by 21 copper strips, 8-pin d.i.l. holder (2 off), large control knob, multi-strand connecting wire, single-sided solder pins, solder, etc.

Chapter 2

ACCESSORIES

In this chapter we will consider a number of electronic accessories for model railways, including several practical projects. These include a points controller, automatic signals, sound effects generators, and an electronic track "cleaner."

To The Point

Electric points are ideal for large and complex layouts as they enable the entire system to be controlled from a single place. Even on the most simple of layouts the use of an electric point can make the system easier and more fun to use.

Electric points are basically quite simple devices which utilize two solenoids (electromagnets), one being used to set the point, and the other to reset it to its original position. In order to change the point from one setting to another it is merely necessary to apply a brief but strong burst of power to the appropriate solenoid.

A point controller can merely consist of a couple of pushbutton switches, as shown in Figure 2.1. Note that although the point contains two solenoids, it normally only has three terminals since one of these is common to both solenoids. Most points have a line of three terminals, with the middle terminal connecting to both solenoids. The point will operate perfectly well from an a.c. supply, so there is no need to rectify or smooth the 15 volt a.c. supply. The latter can be supplied by a mains transformer or, where appropriate, it can be provided by the auxiliary output of the controller. Of course, a d.c. supply of 12 volts or so is equally suitable.

The power is applied to the appropriate solenoid by operating PB1 or PB2. However, care must be taken not to apply the power for too long, as the solenoids have a low impedance and consume a heavy current of at least one amp. Some consume a current of around two amps or so. Excessive operation of a pushbutton switch could result in the solenoid it controls being burnt out. Another problem with this simple arrangement is that the switches have to control quite high currents, and must

51

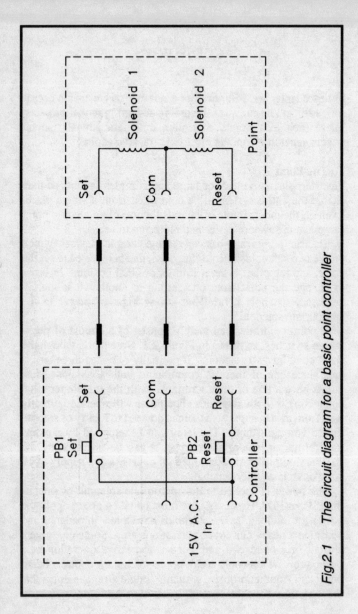

Fig.2.1   The circuit diagram for a basic point controller

52

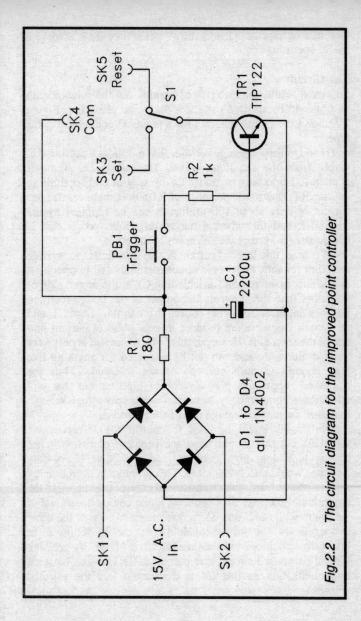

Fig.2.2   The circuit diagram for the improved point controller

53

therefore be expensive heavy-duty types if they are to achieve a useful operating life.

The Circuit

Improved results with no risk of burning out the solenoid can be obtained by using a capacitor discharge controller. Figure 2.2 shows the circuit diagram for a practical controller of this type.

D1 to D4 form a bridge rectifier that produces a pulsing d.c. output from the a.c. input signal. The rough d.c. signal is applied to smoothing capacitor C1 by way of current limiting resistor R1. Due to the presence of R1 a maximum continuous current of only about 100 milliamps can be supplied by the controller, and this gives a maximum output power that is inadequate to damage the solenoids in the point.

Of course, this level of current is also insufficient to activate the point reliably, and would almost certainly fail to operate it at all. This is the reason for including C1 at the output side of R1 rather than direct across the output of the bridge rectifier. R1 does not limit the output current that can flow from C1, and the circuit can therefore produce a large pulse of current into one of the solenoids. However, this pulse of current is only very short in duration, and can not be sustained for anything like long enough to burn out one of the solenoids. Thus the smoothed supply can give a pulse of high current that will operate the point reliably, but it can not supply a high enough sustained current to damage one of the solenoids.

The supply could be used to control the solenoids via switches, but this would leave the problem of the switches having to handle high currents, and expensive heavy-duty switches would still be required. This problem is overcome by using a power Darlington transistor to control the supply to the appropriate solenoid. SK4 connects to the common terminal of the point, while SK3 and SK5 connect one to each of the other two terminals. The desired solenoid is selected by setting S1 to the correct position, and then the circuit is "fired" by pressing PB1. This gives a strong base current to TR1, which biases it into conduction so that C1 is discharged into the selected solenoid.

The current switched by PB1 is far lower than the current fed to the solenoid. In fact it is likely to be no more than about 20 milliamps or so, which can be switched reliably by even the cheapest of pushbutton switches. Admittedly S1 does have to handle the full output current of the controller, but only once it is already closed. Therefore, sparking should not occur at the contacts of this switch, even if it is not a heavy-duty type, and it should have a long operating life. Incidentally, all "real world" switches can handle a much higher current once they are closed than they can handle when switching a current on and off.

Details of the component layout, hard wiring, and underside of the stripboard panel are provided in Figures 2.3 and 2.4. The board has 32 holes by 17 copper strips. Construction of the board is perfectly straightforward, but be careful to fit D1 and the four rectifiers with the correct polarity. Also, do not overlook the single break on the underside of the board. Due to the very intermittent nature of the signal handled by the TR1 it is not necessary to use a heatsink for this component. The hard wiring, etc., is also very straightforward, and this project is simple enough for a complete beginner to tackle.

Components for Figure 2.2

Resistors
R1   180R 2 watt 10% carbon
R2   1k 5% 0.25 watt carbon

Capacitor
C1   2200µ 25V radial electrolytic

Semiconductors
TR1   TIP122 or TIP121
D1 to D4   1N4002 (4 off)

Miscellaneous
PB1   Push-to-make pushbutton switch
S1   S.P.D.T. toggle switch
SK1 to SK5 4mm sockets or terminal posts
Case, 0.1 inch matrix stripboard having 32 holes by 17 copper strips, solder, connecting wire, etc.

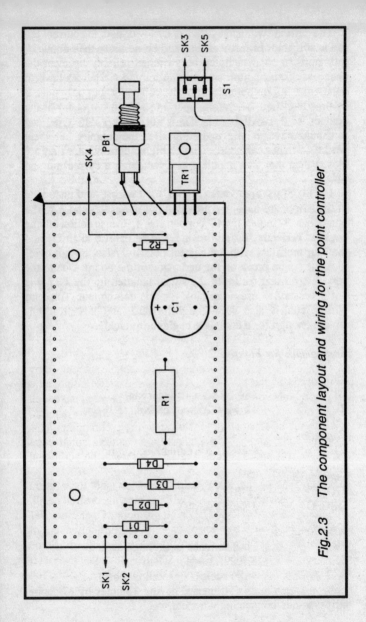

Fig.2.3   The component layout and wiring for the point controller

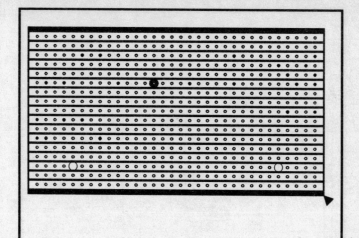

Fig.2.4   The underside of the point controller board

Multi-Point Control

As described so far the controller is only capable of controlling a single point. One solution to controlling several points is to have a separate controller for each one. This is very convenient in use, but is a rather expensive solution. The cheaper alternative is to modify the controller for use with several points. This is easily done, and it is just a matter of adding some extra output sockets and switches. Figure 2.5 shows the additional circuitry needed.

Simply adding an extra set/reset switch and three extra sockets for each additional point will not give the desired result. This gives no way of operating a single point. Operating PB1 will set or reset all the points at once, in the unlikely event of the shared current gives enough power to each point. Some extra switching is needed so that the desired point can be selected. The solution used in Figure 2.5 is to have a pushbutton switch connected in series with each "Com" output of the controller.

57

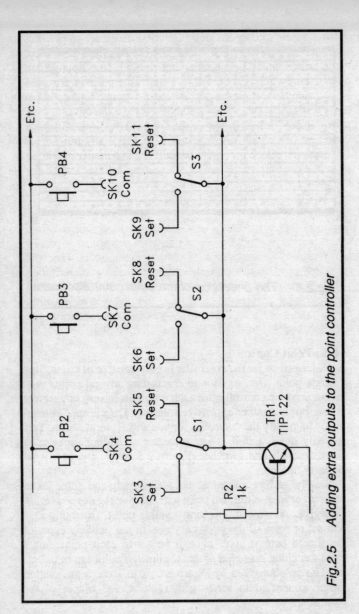

Fig.2.5   Adding extra outputs to the point controller

To alter the setting of a point it is first necessary to give the appropriate set/reset switch the required setting, and then select the required point by pressing and holding the appropriate pushbutton switch (PB2 to PB4). Finally, the point is activated by pressing PB1. If preferred, PB2 to PB4 can be replaced by a three way rotary switch, but pushbuttons have the advantage of giving instant access to any of the controlled points. Although three sets of outputs are shown in Figure 2.5, any number of extra outputs can be accommodated. It is just a matter of adding three sockets, a pushbutton switch, and a set/reset switch for each point.

Automatic Signal

This simple circuit controls a two-colour (red and green) signal, and it automatically switches to red when the signal is passed by the train. It is automatically reset to green again when the train has progressed along the track to some predetermined point. Obviously the circuit requires some means of detecting the train as it passes the signal and the changeover position further along the line. There are two simple approaches to the problem, and one of these is to use a micro-switch.

A micro-switch is basically just an ordinary switch, but instead of having manual operation via a push-button, slider knob, or whatever, it has some sort of lever mechanism that is operated automatically. A micro-switch can be used as a model train sensor if the lever can be positioned where it will be activated by the passing train. In practice it is often difficult to obtain reliable results using this method, and if you get things slightly wrong there can be frequent derailments! Micro-switches can be used as model train sensors, but are not my first choice.

Reed switches are a more popular method of sensing for model train applications, and are my preferred method. A reed switch is basically just two small pieces of springy metal that overlap one another, as in Figure 2.6. These pieces of metal are the "reeds", and they are normally fitted in a glass envelope. The reeds are spaced slightly apart so that they are not quite in electrical contact with each other. If you look carefully at one of these switches you should be able to see the reeds and the gap through the glass casing.

59

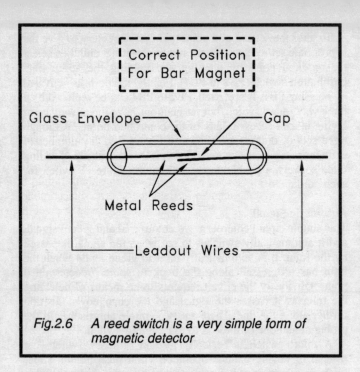

Fig.2.6   A reed switch is a very simple form of
magnetic detector

If a reasonably strong bar magnet is placed next to a reed switch, the two reeds become temporarily magnetised by the field of the magnet. The two ends of the reeds that are in close proximity to each other have opposite poles, and accordingly they are attracted to one another. Due to the flexible nature of the reeds, this results in the overlapping ends moving together and touching, so that electrical contact is completed. This gives a simple switching action, with the switch open when the magnet is absent, and closed when it is brought close to the reeds. The contact ratings of reed switches are very low incidentally, but they are more than adequate for position sensing, where they will typically handle only about five to 10 milliamps at five to 12 volts d.c.

The magnet must normally be within about 20 to 30 millimetres of the reed switch before the latter will be activated. Although this gives a very short operating range, it is sufficient for use in computerised model train systems, and many other computer control applications. An important factor in favour of this system for model train use is that there is no need for any direct contact between the train and the sensor. This totally avoids any problems with the sensors causing derailments.

Positioning of the bar magnet is crucial, and the reed switch will simply not operate if the relative orientation of the magnet is not correct. The magnet must be parallel to the switch, as shown in Figure 2.6. Having the magnet perpendicular to the reeds will not close the switch even at point-blank range. In model train applications the reed switch is often placed under the track, and the magnet is fitted in the base of a piece of rolling stock. If the reed switch is fitted across the track, then the magnet must be fitted across the carriage or truck. My preference is to have the reed switch running along the middle of the track. The magnet must then be fitted lengthwise along the base section of the piece of rolling stock, and not across it.

Of course, the motors in model trains contain permanent magnets, and it is possible that one of these will activate the reed switch if it is placed in a suitable position on the track. In practice this method only seems to work in a small minority of cases, and it is probably better to simply add a bar magnet to the train rather than spending a great deal of time trying to utilize the magnet in the electric motor.

The Circuit
The circuit diagram for the automatic train signal appears in Figure 2.7. The circuit is really just a basic bistable multivibrator, which is a form of simple memory circuit. At switch-on one transistor will switch on and the other will switch off. There is no way of knowing which transistor will switch on, but here we will assume that it is TR2. This results in TR2 supplying a strong current to D6, which is the green signal LED. With TR2 switched on, its collector voltage is very low, and TR1 receives no significant base current via R4. Consequently, TR1 is switched off, and D5 (the red signal LED) receives only an insignificant current.

S2 is the reed or micro-switch positioned next to the signal. S2 closes momentarily as it is passed by the train, and in doing

61

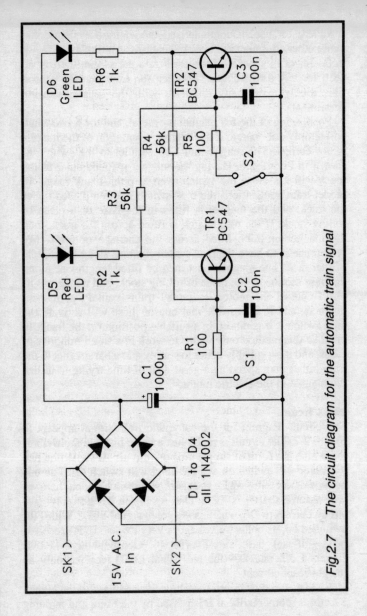

Fig.2.7   The circuit diagram for the automatic train signal

so it diverts practically all of TR2's base current to earth via R5. This results in TR2 switching off, which in turn results in D6 being switched off. The collector of TR2 now goes to virtually the full positive supply voltage, and TR1 is biased into conduction by the base current it receives through R4. This switches on D5 so that a "red" signal is produced.

Once the train has passed and S2 opens again, TR2 remains switched off because TR1's collector is at a very low potential. TR2 therefore receives no significant base current via R3. The train then proceeds along the track, until it eventually reaches S1. When S1 closes, TR1 becomes switched off, and TR2 is then biased into conduction by the base current it receives via R3. This switches off D5 and switches on D6, giving a "green" indication from the signal. The circuit stays in this state even when S1 opens again, because the collector of TR2 is at a low voltage, and no significant base current is supplied to TR1 by way of R4.

This basic sequence of events is repeated indefinitely as the train moves around the track, with the signal switching to "red" as the train passes the signal, and back to "green" again as the train passes S1. C2 and C3 help to avoid problems with spurious triggering due to pickup of electrical noise in the connecting leads to S1 and S2. Even with C2 and C3 included in the circuit, it would be advisable to use screened lead to carry the connections from the main unit to S1 and S2. The outer braiding should connect to the 0 volt earth rail, and the inner conductors should connect to R1 and R5. R1 and R5 also help to filter out any electrical noise which might otherwise give problems with spurious triggering, and they also provide current limiting which helps to protect S1 and S2. If manual control of the signal is required, simply wire push-to-make pushbutton switches in parallel with S1 and S2.

The circuit is powered from a 15 volt a.c. supply via the bridge rectifier formed by D1 to D4, and smoothing capacitor C1. This gives a reasonably well smoothed d.c. supply to the main circuit, which does not require a particularly stable or ripple-free supply. The current consumption of the circuit is about 20 milliamps, which is also the approximate current fed to whichever LED is switched on. This current is adequate

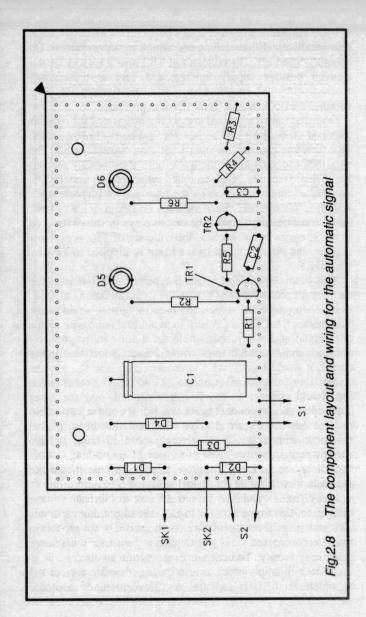

Fig.2.8   The component layout and wiring for the automatic signal

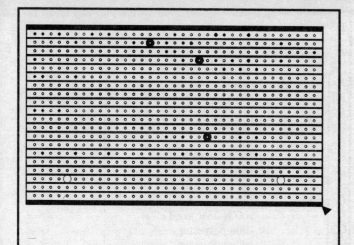

*Fig.2.9   The underside view of the automatic
signal board*

to give good brightness without having to resort to "high-brightness" LEDs.

Construction

The stripboard component layout and wiring for the automatic signal is shown in Figure 2.8. The underside view of the board appears in Figure 2.9. The board measure 35 holes by 20 copper strips. Construction of this board offers nothing out of the ordinary, and it is another project that a beginner should be able to tackle. Building the model signal will require a bit of ingenuity, but it should not be too difficult to fabricate something reasonably convincing from balsa wood and other normal craft materials. Three millimetre diameter LEDs are probably the best choice for 00 gauge layouts. The five millimetre diameter type might be better for larger gauge layouts.

I used a Maplin "large" magnet mounted under a piece of rolling stock, and Maplin "miniature" reed switches mounted under the track. However, it should be possible to get reliable operation using practically any reed switch plus any small but powerful bar magnet.

Components for Figure 2.7

Resistors (all 0.25 watt 5% carbon film)
R1	100R
R2	1k
R3	56k
R4	56k
R5	100R
R6	1k

Capacitors
C1	1000µ 25V axial elect
C2	100n polyester
C3	100n polyester

Semiconductors
TR1	BC547
TR2	BC547
D1 to D4	1N4002 (4 off)
D5	Red LED
D6	Green LED

Miscellaneous
S1	s.p.s.t. micro-switch or reed switch
S2	s.p.s.t. micro-switch or reed switch
SK1	4mm socket or terminal post
SK2	4mm socket or terminal post

Case, 0.1 inch matrix stripboard measuring 35 holes by 20 strips, solder, screened cable, multi-strand connecting wire, solder, small bar magnet (see text), etc.

Signal Controller
This project could be regarded as the inverse of the previous one, since it is a device that causes the train to automatically obey a signal, rather than a signal that is controlled by the train. Thus, if you set the signal to "red" the train will come to a halt

just in front of the signal. Setting the signal to "green" causes the train to pull away and continue on its journey. If the signal is at green as the train approaches it, the train continues on its way. Neither the drawing to a halt or acceleration away from the signal are too abrupt, and this is achieved by using this unit in conjunction with a controller that provides simulated inertia, momentum, and braking. In fact this circuit is an add-on for a version of the "improved" pulsed train controller circuit (Figures 1.21 and 1.25) which is described in Chapter One of this publication.

At first thought one might think that all the controller has to do is stop the train when the signal is set to "red", and start it again when the signal is set to "green". Unfortunately, things are not quite as simple as this. The train must only stop when the signal is at "red" and the train is approaching the signal. The train should not stop wherever it happens to be just because the signal is at "red".

For the system to work properly it is essential to include a sensor that enables the controller to detect that the train is approaching the signal. A hold-off can then be used to prevent the train from being brought to a halt until the signal is at "red", and the train is at the appropriate position on the track. The position sensing is achieved using a magnet and a reed switch (or a micro-switch if preferred), as used in the automatic signal project.

The Circuit

Figure 2.10 shows the circuit diagram for the signal controller. Like the automatic signal, this unit is based on a bistable circuit. This has TR2 and TR3 in the standard bistable configuration. Bistable operation was covered in the previous section of this book, and it will not be covered again here.

When S1 is in the "green" position, the base of TR2 is connected to the 0 volt rail by S1a, forcing the bistable into the state where the collector of TR2 is high, and the collector of TR3 is low. With the collector of TR3 low, TR1 is cut off, and it has no significant affect on the pulsed controller circuit. S1b connects power to the green signal LED (D1) via current limiting resistor R7. The latter sets the LED current at roughly 20 milliamps.

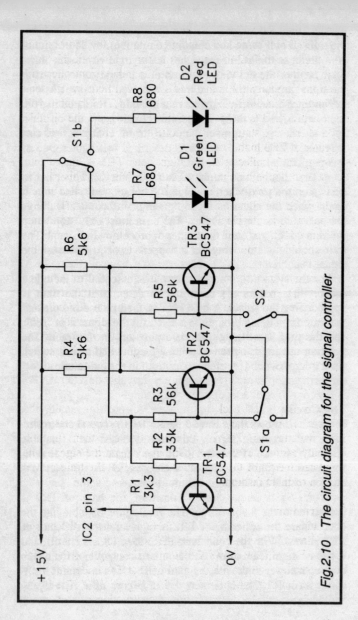

Fig.2.10 The circuit diagram for the signal controller

If S1 is set to the "red" position, D1 is switched off and the red LED (D2) is turned on. Also, S1a removes the short circuit from the base of TR2 to the 0 volt supply. However, this does not alter the state of the bistable, and the pulsed controller still functions normally. S2 is the reed switch or micro-switch sensor, and it momentarily connects the base of TR3 to the 0 volt rail when it detects the passing train. This triggers the bistable to its alternative state, with the collector of TR2 low, and the collector of TR3 high.

With TR3's collector in the high state, TR1 is biased into conduction by the base current it receives via R2. This has the effect of rapidly discharging C4 in the pulsed controller circuit via R1 in this circuit, and R8 in the controller circuit. The discharge rate is far higher than is really needed, which results in the train coming to a fairly rapid halt.

A more gradual reduction in speed can be obtained by increasing the value of R8 in the pulsed controller circuit. A value of about 47k seems to give quite good results. A higher value will give a more gradual deceleration, but this makes it more difficult to get the train to halt close to the desired spot, just in front of the signal. In fact it will only be possible if the train is run at just the right speed. Using a faster rate of deceleration makes it much easier to get the train to stop close to the right spot, and also gives a certain amount of latitude in the normal running speed of the train. It is probably best to set VR1 in the controller at a medium speed setting.

When S1 is set back to the "green" position again, the bistable is immediately forced back to its original state, and TR1 switches off. The pulsed controller can then function normally again, and the train pulls away from the signal. The simulated inertia of the controller ensures that the train moves off in a realistic fashion.

Construction

This add-on circuit is housed in the same case as the pulsed controller, and is powered from the controller's 15 volt d.c. supply. Figure 2.11 shows the component layout of the stripboard panel, together with the hard wiring. The underside view of the stripboard panel is provided in Figure 2.12. The board has 31 holes by 18 copper strips. Construction of the circuit

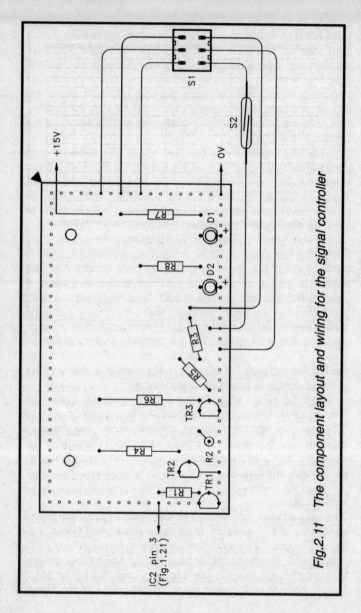

Fig.2.11   The component layout and wiring for the signal controller

70

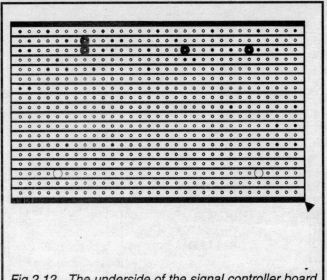

Fig.2.12 The underside of the signal controller board

board offers nothing out of the ordinary. Of course, D1 and D2 are shown as being mounted on the circuit board in Figure 2.11, but in practice they are obviously mounted in the signal.

A lead from this add-on board to the main controller board is required. This connection is to pin 3 of IC2 in the pulsed controller circuit. This connection can be made at any of the four holes to the left of IC2 pin 3 on the pulsed controller board. Do not forget that the value of R8 on the main board must be increased from 10k to around 47k in order to give a reasonably slow deceleration rate.

A little experimentation is needed in order to find a suitable position on the track for S2. Remember that the speed set using VR1 in the pulsed controller will have a large affect on the train's stopping distance, and that a given position for S2 will only give satisfactory results over a certain range of speed settings.

71

Components for Figure 2.10

Resistors (all 0.25 watt 5% carbon film)

R1	3k3
R2	33k
R3	56k
R4	5k6
R5	56k
R6	5k6
R7	680R
R8	680R

Semiconductors

TR1	BC547
TR2	BC547
TR3	BC547
D1	Green LED
D2	Red LED

Miscellaneous

S1	d.p.d.t. min toggle
S2	reed or micro-switch

0.1 inch matrix stripboard having 31 holes by 18 copper strips, multi-strand connecting wire, solder-pins, solder, etc.

Note that additionally a full set of components for the "improved" pulsed controller are required (Figures 2.21 and 1.25). Also, R8 in the pulsed controller should be changed from 10k to about 47k.

Electronic Steam Whistle

When used in conjunction with a suitable amplifier and loud-speaker, this circuit gives a simulation of a steam train whistle. Although you might think that a simple tone generator is all that is needed in order to give a reasonably convincing simulation of a steam train whistle, in reality things are not quite as simple as that.

One problem with a simple tone generator is that it has almost instant attack and decay times. In other words, the tone jumps almost instantly to full volume when you switch the

72

circuit on, and it ceases almost at once when it is switched off again. The volume of steam whistle has a rather more gradual build-up to its normal level. The fall to zero at the end is quite rapid, but it is considerably less than instant. There are no precise rise and fall times which we should try to simulate, since the characteristics of steam whistles vary somewhat from one to another. There is a considerable degree of latitude available here.

Another characteristic of steam whistles is a change of pitch during the rise and fall times. The pitch usually increases quite significantly during the rise time, and decreases during the fall time. However, some whistles seem to change in the opposite fashion, and others seem to provide a relatively stable note. This is presumably a factor that depends on the precise design of the whistle.

There is a third characteristic of a steam whistle that must be taken into account. This is the fact that the purity of the note changes during the rise and fall times. Initially the note is very pure and is virtually a sinewave, but there is an increase in the harmonic content of the sound as the volume builds up. Harmonics are simply sounds at multiples of the fundamental frequency, and strong harmonics produce a much more harsh sound. As the sound decays the opposite occurs, with the harmonic content of the sound diminishing.

One final characteristic of importance is that there is a background "hissing" noise caused by the steam which drives the whistle. It is necessary to mix a "hissing" noise sound with the tone signal in order to simulate a steam whistle reasonably well.

A circuit to produce a highly accurate simulation of a steam whistle would be quite complex, with voltage controlled attenuators, a voltage controlled oscillator, a noise generator, various filters, etc. In fact it would probably be easier to use a circuit containing a digital recording of a real steam whistle sound! The circuit featured here has been kept very simple, but it still provides a reasonably convincing steam whistle sound. However, do not expect results that will genuinely rival the sort of sound effects possible with a 16-bit computer sound card.

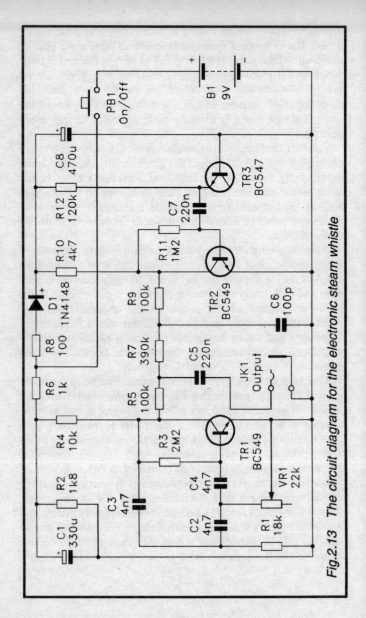

Fig.2.13 The circuit diagram for the electronic steam whistle

The Circuit

The full circuit diagram for the steam whistle simulator is shown in Figure 2.13. The circuit really breaks down into three sections, which are the tone generator, the noise source, and a simple mixer which combines the two signals.

TR1 is used as the basis of the tone generator, and this is used in a simple phase shift oscillator. TR1 operates as a high gain common emitter amplifier having R4 as its collector load and R3 to provide base biasing. The phase shift network is comprised of R1, VR1, the input impedance of TR1, and C2 to C4. It is connected between the output and input of TR1. At a particular frequency the phase shift network provides a phase shift of 180 degrees, which is the phase shift produced by TR1 at all frequencies within its operating range. At the frequency where there is a 180 degree change through the phase shift network, the inversion through TR1 is effectively cancelled out by the inversion through the phase shift network. This gives positive feedback over TR1, and provided the gain through TR1 exceeds the losses through the phase shift network, the circuit will oscillate.

With VR1 set towards maximum value the gain through TR1 is substantially greater than the losses through the phase shift network. This gives strong oscillation, and a clipped sinewave signal at TR1's collector. Adjusting VR1 for a lower resistance results in larger losses through the phase shift network, giving an improvement in the purity of the sinewave output signal. It also results in a rise in the frequency of the output signal. If the resistance through VR1 is set too low, the losses through the phase shift network become too great, and oscillation subsides.

In practice VR1 is given a setting that is just high enough in value to give reasonably strong oscillation, and a noticeable harmonic content on the output signal.When PB1 is operated, power is applied to the circuit via the C – R timing circuit comprised of R6 and C1. This gives a gradual build-up in the supply voltage to the oscillator, and it takes about half a second for the full supply potential to be reached. This limits the output level from the oscillator when PB1 is initially operated, and gives the required build-up in volume. As the supply voltage builds up, the gain of TR1 also increases. This results in the circuit oscillating less strongly initially, with the output signal

75

therefore having higher purity initially. Thus, in addition to the gradual rise in volume, the required steady increase in harmonic content is also obtained.

When PB1 is released, the voltage across C1 decays, causing the amplitude of the output signal to gradually fall away and the purity of the output signal to improve. R2 ensures that the decay time, which would otherwise be slightly excessive, is kept suitably short. The decay time is likely to be several seconds if R2 is omitted.

The noise signal is generated by R12 and TR3, with the reverse biased base – emitter junction of TR3 acting rather like a zener diode. In common with a zener diode, TR3 produces a relatively high noise level. In fact a reverse biased base – emitter junction seems to provide substantially more noise over the audio range than a zener diode. Although transistors operating at low currents are normally associated with low noise levels, in this case a fairly low current seems to give the strongest noise signal. Load resistor R12 has therefore been given a relatively high value. Although a BC547 transistor has been specified for TR3, virtually any high gain silicon n.p.n. transistor will work well as a noise source. Probably many constructors will have a suitable device in their spares box.

TR3 produces a high output level by the standards of noise sources, but in absolute terms the signal level at the emitter of TR3 is quite low. In fact it will be no more than a few millivolts r.m.s. TR2 is therefore used as a high gain common emitter amplifier which boosts the noise signal to a level that is roughly comparable to the output level from TR1. The noise generator circuit is fed from the main supply via R8, D1, and C8. The low value of R8 results in the circuit having a fast attack time, with the noise signal reaching full volume almost as soon as PB1 is operated. This is in keeping with the rapid introduction of the "hiss" sound when a steam whistle is operated. D1 prevents C8 from discharging through R8 and into the tone generator circuit when PB1 is released. The decay time of the noise generator is therefore much longer than the attack time, with the "hiss" sound being sustained for at least as long as the tone signal. This is again in keeping with the sound of a real steam whistle.

The output signal from TR2 contains a slightly excessive

high frequency content. R9 and C6 are therefore used as a simple lowpass filter which gives a small reduction in the high frequency content of the noise signal. R5 and R7 form a simple passive mixer circuit which combines the tone and noise signals to produce a single output signal. R7 has been made higher in value than R5 so that the noise signal is kept at a lower level than the tone signal. In order to obtain a convincing effect the "hiss" sound must be in the background, with the audio tone providing the major part of the output signal. C5 provides d.c. blocking at the output of the unit.

A supply potential of about 9 to 12 volts is needed. The supply should not be much less than about 9 volts or the reverse base – emitter breakdown voltage of TR3 may not be reached, and no noise output signal would then be generated. The current consumption of the circuit is only about 1.5 milliamps, and a PP3 size 9 volt battery is probably the most practical power source.

Ideally the circuit should feed into an input which has a fairly high input impedance and low sensitivity. An input intended for a crystal or ceramic pick-up should be ideal. The unit also seems to work quite well with "tuner" inputs and the like, which have slightly higher sensitivities but lower input impedances. It should therefore be possible to use this circuit successfully with virtually any power amplifier.

To some extent the characteristics of the sound generated by the unit can be adjusted by altering the values of certain components. The attack and decay times of the tone generator circuit can be increased and decreased by altering the value of C1. Increased values give proportionately longer attack and decay times, and lower values give proportionately shorter times. The decay time can be lengthened without significantly affecting the attack time by increasing the value of R2. The decay time can be shortened by reducing the value of R2, but there is little latitude available here, since reducing the value of this component reduces the supply voltage to the tone generator. More than a slight reduction in the value of R2 could result in an inadequate supply voltage to the oscillator circuit.

The amount of noise signal added into the audio tone can be altered by changing the value of R7. Use a lower value to increase the level of the noise signal, or a higher value to reduce it. The tone generator operates at a frequency of about 1kHz or so, but other frequencies can be obtained by using a different value for C2 to C4. The output frequency is inversely proportional to the value used for C2 to C4 (e.g. a value of 10n gives an output frequency of about 500Hz). C2 to C4 should all have the same value.

Construction

Virtually any small plastic or metal case should be adequate to accommodate this project, complete with a PP3 size battery. VR1, PB1, and JK1 are mounted on the front panel or lid of the case. A 3.5 millimetre jack socket is used for JK1 on the prototype, but it is obviously in order to use a phono socket or any other type that is a better match for your audio equipment.

Figure 2.14 shows the component layout for the stripboard panel, together with details of the small amount of hard wiring. The underside view of the board appears in Figure 2.15. The board measures 30 holes by 17 copper strips. Building this board is slightly more difficult than constructing most of those featured previously in this book, because the component density is somewhat higher. Several of the resistors are mounted vertically. However, construction should be trouble-free provided you proceed with due care and attention. Do not forget the four breaks in the copper strips on the underside of the board. From the electrical point of view, C2 to C4 can be any plastic foil capacitors (polyester, polycarbonate, mylar, etc.). To fit easily into the layout these capacitors must have reasonably long leadout wires, which makes mylar capacitors a good choice.

The optimum setting for VR1 is found by trial and error. If it is set too low in value (adjusted too far in a counter-clockwise direction) either oscillation will not occur, or it will be barely achieved. Setting VR1 too high in value will give strong oscillation, and there will be little change in the harmonic content of the output signal during the attack and decay periods. There should be a small range of intermediate settings that give the desired effect.

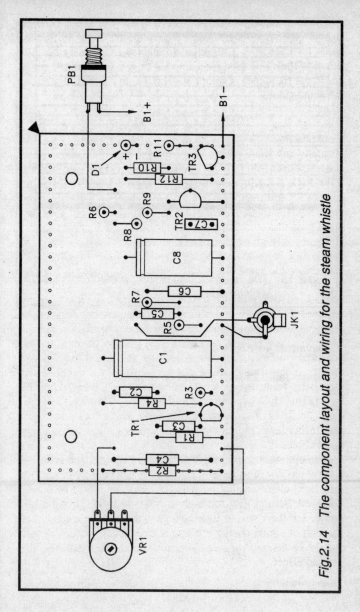

Fig.2.14   The component layout and wiring for the steam whistle

Fig.2.15   The underside view of the electronic steam whistle board

Components for Figure 2.13

Resistors (all 0.25 watt 5% carbon film)
R1	18k
R2	1k8
R3	2M2
R4	10k
R5	100k
R6	1k
R7	390k
R8	100R
R9	100k
R10	4k7
R11	1M2
R12	120k

Potentiometer
VR1	22k lin carbon

80

Capacitors

C1	330µ 16V axial elect
C2	4n7 mylar
C3	4n7 mylar
C4	4n7 mylar
C5	220n polyester
C6	100p ceramic plate
C7	220n polyester
C8	470µ 16V axial elect

Semiconductors

TR1	BC549
TR2	BC549
TR3	BC547 (see text)
D1	1N4148

Miscellaneous

PB1	Push-to-make pushbutton switch
B1	9 volt (PP3 size)
JK1	3.5mm jack socket (see text)

Case, 0.1 inch matrix stripboard panel 30 holes by 17 copper strips, control knob, battery connector, multi-strand connecting wire, solder, etc.

Two Tone Horn

This extremely simply circuit gives a rough simulation of the two tone horn fitted to diesel locomotives. These usually produce an initial tone of low purity and rapid rise-time, followed by a tone of similar purity and about 50% higher in pitch. The second tone is usually of relatively short duration and has a fall-time which is significantly longer than the rise-time.

The Circuit

The complete circuit diagram for the two tone train horn appears in Figure 2.16. As will be immediately apparent to many readers, the circuit is basically just a 555 timer used in the standard astable configuration. The 555 timer has a sufficiently powerful output stage to drive a high impedance loudspeaker at good volume, and it is not necessary to use a

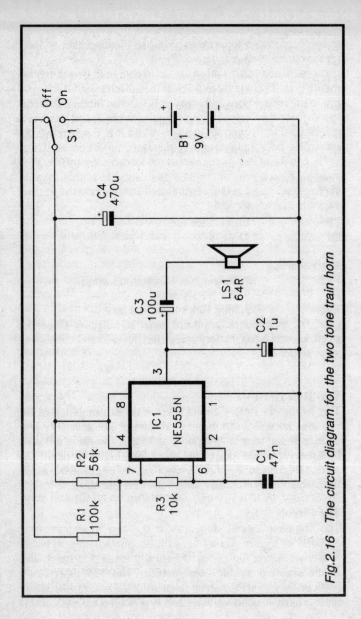

Fig.2.16   The circuit diagram for the two tone train horn

separate amplifier. Of course, if preferred, the output of the unit can be coupled to a separate amplifier and loudspeaker so that higher volume levels can be achieved.

IC1 oscillates by first allowing C1 to charge to two-thirds of the supply voltage via R2 and R3. It then discharges C1 to one-third of the supply voltage by way of R3 and an internal switching transistor. The output of the device is at pin 3, and this goes high while C1 is charging, and low while it is discharging. A rectangular output waveform is therefore produced at IC1's output, and this signal is coupled to the loudspeaker by C3. The harmonic content on the output signal is rather higher than is really needed, and C2 is therefore used to attenuate the higher frequency harmonics.

C4 is a supply decoupling capacitor, and it has purposely been made rather higher in value than would normally be the case. When on/off switch S1 is set to the "on" position, C4 rapidly charges from the low source impedance of the battery. This gives the output signal a fairly fast, but less than instant attack time, which is what is required in this case. The audio tone is then emitted from LS1 for as long as S1 is held in the "on" position, which in practice should be roughly one second.

When S1 is returned to the "off" position the tone does not cut off at once, since C4 provides enough power to sustain oscillation for about half a second. S1 now shunts R1 across R2, giving a reduction in the circuit's timing resistance, and a consequent increase in the pitch of the output signal. This gives the required two tone effect, and a relatively slow fall-time to the signal. Ideally S1 should be a biased switch, biased to the "off" position, but obviously a non-biased type can be used if preferred, or if a biased type proves to be difficult to obtain.

The current consumption of the circuit is about 20 milliamps. This can be provided economically by a PP3 size battery since the unit will only be switched on briefly and very intermittently.

Construction

The unit is housed in a small plastic or metal case with S1 and LS1 mounted on the front panel. The loudspeaker requires a grille, and this is probably produced most easily by drilling a matrix of small holes. Miniature loudspeakers rarely have

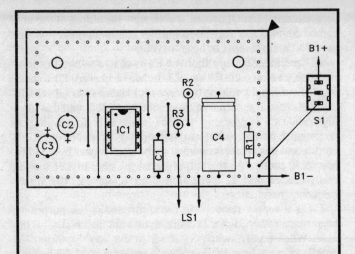

Fig.2.17   The component layout and wiring for the
two tone train horn

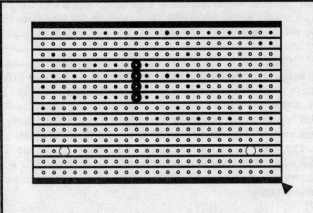

Fig.2.18   The underside of the two tone train horn

84

provision for fixing screws, and this leaves little option but to glue LS1 in place. Any good quality general purpose adhesive should fix it reliably, but be careful not to smear the adhesive onto the diaphragm. Note that LS1 must be a high impedance type having an impedance of around 40 to 80 ohms. A low impedance loudspeaker, such as an ordinary 8 ohm type, would almost certainly place excessive loading on the output stage of IC1.

Apart from the battery, the other components are fitted onto a 0.1 inch pitch stripboard which has 23 holes by 14 copper strips. Figure 1.17 shows the component layout for the circuit board, together with details of the small amount of hard wiring. The underside view of the board appears in Figure 2.18. The 555 is not a static-sensitive device, but I would still recommend the use of a holder for this component. Note that IC1 must be a standard 555 and not one of the low power versions of the 555. Low power versions of the 555 mostly seem to have output stages that do not function well when driving a loudspeaker.

Components for Figure 2.16

Resistors (all 0.25 watt 5% carbon film)
R1	100k
R2	56k
R3	10k

Capacitors
C1	47n polyester
C2	1µ 50V radial elect
C3	100µ 10V radial elect
C4	470µ 10V axial elect

Semiconductor
IC1	NE555N

Miscellaneous
LS1	64 ohm miniature loudspeaker (see text)
B1	9 volt (PP3 size)
S1	s.p.d.t. (see text)

Case, 0.1 inch matrix stripboard having 23 holes by 14 copper strips, 8-pin d.i.l. holder, battery connector, multi-strand connecting wire, solder, etc.

Automatic Train Horn

This circuit provides basically the same function as the train horn described in the previous section, but it operates automatically each time the train passes a certain point on the track. The circuit is triggered by a reed switch or micro-switch on the track, like the automatic signals featured at the beginning of this chapter. The sensor switch will only operate very briefly as the train passes, which requires a substantially more complex circuit than when using manual operation.

The block diagram of Figure 2.19 shows the general scheme of things used in this unit. The sensor switch drives two mono-stables, and these both operate as pulse stretchers. Once triggered by the sensor switch the upper monostable produces an output pulse of about 1.7 seconds in duration. During this period it turns on the tone generator, which it controls via a buffer amplifier. This gives the required burst of tone, but without the two tone effect.

The second monostable is used to control the pitch of the tone generator, and provide the two tone effect. The tone generator is a form of v.c.o. (voltage controlled oscillator), and its control voltage is provided by the output of the second monostable. When triggered, the second monostable produces an output pulse of just under one second. The v.c.o. is a type where a high control voltage produces lower frequencies, and a low control voltage produces higher frequencies.

When the circuit is triggered, the second monostable provides a high control voltage, which results in a relatively low output frequency from the tone generator. After about one second the output pulse from the second monostable ceases, and the lower control voltage to the v.c.o. gives an output signal of increased pitch. About 0.7 seconds or so later the output pulse from the other monostable ends, and the tone is cut off. The circuit thus provides the required two tone effect, with the initial tone lasting just under one second and the higher tone lasting about 0.7 seconds or so.

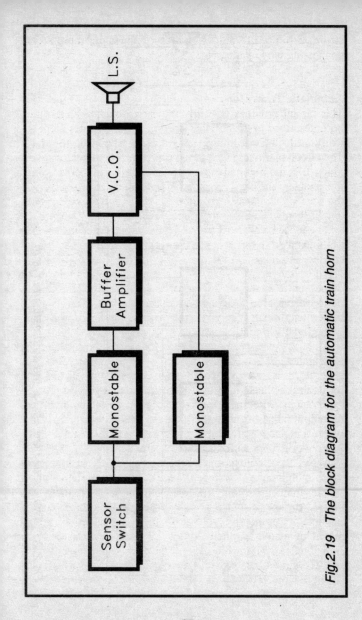

Fig.2.19   The block diagram for the automatic train horn

87

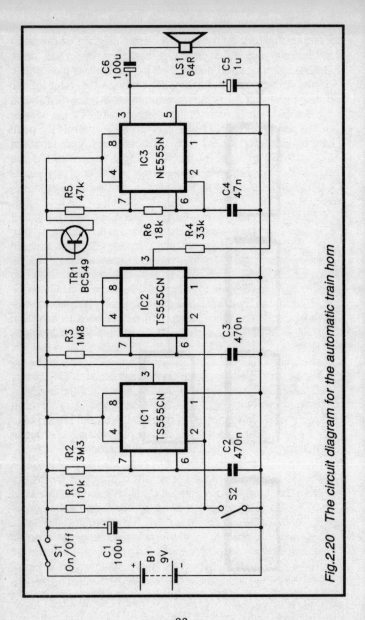

Fig.2.20   The circuit diagram for the automatic train horn

The Circuit

Refer to Figure 2.20 for the full circuit diagram of the automatic train horn. The circuit is based on three 555 timer integrated circuits. IC1 and IC2 are used in the two monostable stages, and these two stages differ only in the value of the timing resistor. IC1 has the larger timing resistance (3M3), and this device is used to control the tone generator. IC2 has a lower timing resistance (1M8) and this monostable controls the pitch of the tone generator. R1 normally holds the trigger inputs of IC1 and IC2 at virtually the full supply voltage. S2 is the sensor switch, and when this closes it pulls the trigger inputs below one third of the supply voltage, activating both monostables.

TR1 acts as an emitter follower buffer stage at the output of IC1, and this enables it to comfortably handle the supply current drawn by the tone generator. The tone generator is based on IC3, which is used in the standard astable mode. In fact the tone generator is basically the same as the one used in the two tone train horn featured in the previous section of this book.

IC2 has a timing resistance of 1M8, giving it a shorter output pulse duration. This device is therefore used to drive the control input of the tone generator. This is pin 5 of IC3, which connects to the internal potential divider that sets the two-thirds of the supply threshold level. It is of course, at this potential that the circuit switches from C4 being charged to C4 starting to discharge. The output of IC2 goes high when the circuit is triggered, and it then pulls the threshold level higher. As a result of this it takes C4 longer to charge to the threshold level, and to discharge back to one third of the supply voltage. The output frequency of the tone generator is therefore reduced.

When the output pulse from IC2 ends, the threshold level is taken to less than its normal level of two-thirds of the supply voltage. It then takes less time for C4 to charge to the threshold level and to discharge back down to one-third of the supply voltage. The output frequency of IC3 therefore increases, giving the required two tone effect. The value of R4 controls the degree of coupling between IC2 and IC3, and it therefore sets the difference between the high and low tones. Use a higher value to reduce the difference in the pitches of the two notes, or a lower value to increase it.

Low power versions of the 555 timer are specified for IC1 and IC2, and any low power version of the device should be suitable. The circuit will work perfectly well with standard 555s, but would have a rather high standby current consumption of about 16 milliamps. Most low power 555s give a quiescent current consumption of under 500 microamps. The quiescent current consumption of the prototype was measured at just under 300 microamps. Although the consumption increases to around 20 milliamps when the unit is activated, a PP3 size battery is still perfectly adequate to power the unit.

Construction
Virtually any medium size plastic or metal case should comfortably accommodate this project. LS1 and S1 are mounted on the front panel, and an exit hole for the lead to S2 must be made in the rear panel. If a metal case is used, this hole should be fitted with a grommet to protect the cable. The 0.1 inch pitch stripboard panel has 42 holes by 20 copper strips. Figure 2.21 shows the component layout and hard wiring, while Figure 2.22 shows the underside view of the board. Construction of the board is very straightforward, but be careful not to overlook any of the link wires. Most low power 555s are based on CMOS technology, but they have internal protection circuitry that renders any special handling precautions unnecessary. However, I would still recommend using holders for all three integrated circuits.

In use it is possible that stray pick-up of electrical noise in the connecting lead to S2 will cause spurious triggering. If this should occur, reducing the value of R1 to about 1k8 should cure the problem.

Components for Figure 2.20

Resistors (all 0.25 watt 5% carbon film)

R1	10k
R2	3M3
R3	1M8
R4	33k
R5	47k
R6	18k

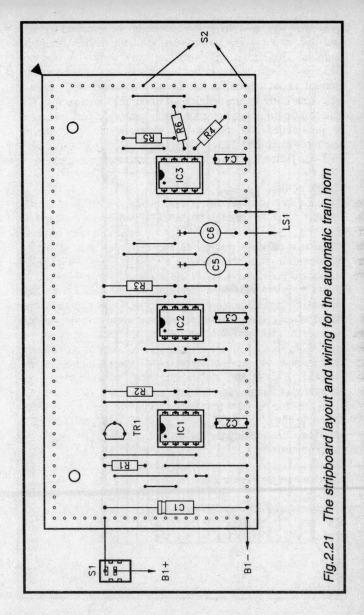

Fig.2.21 The stripboard layout and wiring for the automatic train horn

91

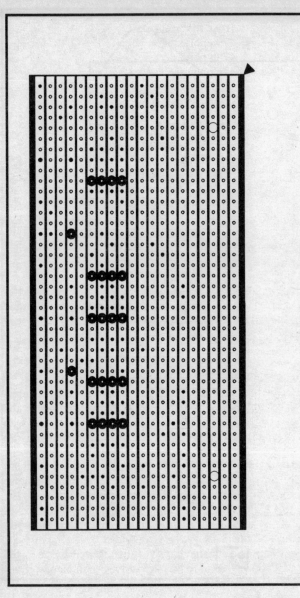

Fig.2.22   The underside of the automatic train horn board

Capacitors

C1	100µ 10V axial elect
C2	470n polyester
C3	470n polyester
C4	47n polyester
C5	1µ 50V radial elect
C6	100µ 10V radial elect

Semiconductors

IC1	TS555CN (see text)
IC2	TS555CN (see text)
IC3	NE555N
TR1	BC549

Miscellaneous

LS1	40 - 80R miniature loudspeaker
S1	s.p.s.t. min toggle switch
S2	reed or micro-switch
B1	9 volt (PP3 size)

Case, 0.1 inch matrix stripboard having 42 holes by 20 strips, 8-pin d.i.l. holder (3 off), battery connector, multi-strand connecting wire, solder, etc.

Automatic Chuffer

This circuit simulates the "chuffing" sound made by a steam train. The "chuff" rate is controlled by the voltage across the track, and it therefore increases and decreases in sympathy with changes in the speed of the train. The block diagram of Figure 2.23 helps to explain the way in which the unit functions.

The basic sound source is a noise generator which produces ordinary "hiss" type noise. As the output level from the noise generator is quite low, an amplifier stage is used to boost the signal to a more useful level. The "chuffing" sound consists of bursts of noise, and these are produced by gating the noise signal on and off. This gating is provided by a simple v.c.a. (voltage controlled attenuator). The output from the v.c.a. is fed to a small power amplifier which drives a miniature loud-speaker at good volume.

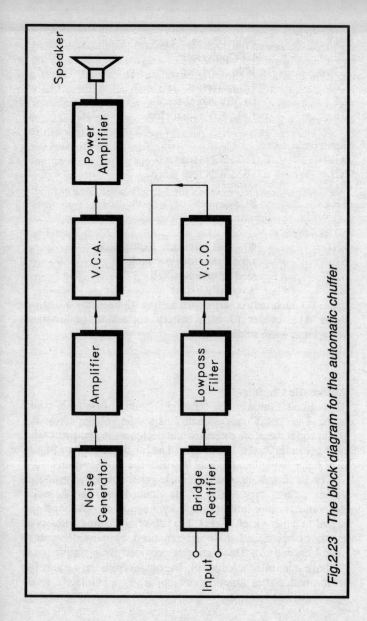

Fig.2.23   The block diagram for the automatic chuffer

The control signal for the v.c.a. is produced by first rectifying the voltage from the track. This ensures that the subsequent stages are always fed with a positive signal regardless of the direction in which the train is travelling. The signal from the track might be a reasonably "clean" d.c. signal, but it is likely to contain a lot of noise spikes generated by the electric motor in the train. Also, if a pulsed controller is used, the signal from the track will obviously be a pulsed type, and not a straightforward d.c. signal. A lowpass filter is therefore used to smooth the output from the bridge rectifier. This gives a low ripple output signal at a level equal to the average input potential.

The output from the lowpass filter is fed to the control input of a v.c.o. (voltage controlled oscillator). The output frequency of this stage is roughly proportional to the applied control voltage. The actual output frequency is zero with no track voltage, or a low track voltage of up to about three volts or so. This gives either a continuous "hissing" sound from the unit, or silence, depending on the output state of the v.c.o. when oscillation ceased. Either of these is acceptable, since the halted train might simply stand quietly until it moves off, or steam may be released in order to prevent excessive pressure building up. The steady "hissing" sound gives quite a good simulation of excess steam being released. At higher track voltages the v.c.o. begins to oscillate, but reaches a frequency that is still no more than a few hertz at maximum track voltage.

The Circuit
Figure 2.24 shows the main circuit for the automatic chuffer, but the noise generator circuit is shown separately in Figure 2.25. Taking the main circuit first, the bridge rectifier is formed by D1 to D4, and the lowpass filtering is provided by R1 and C1. The v.c.o. is based on IC1, which is a CMOS "micropower" phased locked loop. However, in this case only the v.c.o. section is utilized, and no connections are made to the phase comparators or other sections of IC1. C2 and R2 are the timing components.

The control input of IC1 is fed from the output of the lowpass filter via D5, D6, and VR1. The latter is adjusted so that the oscillator starts operating as the train starts to move away. There is a slight problem here in that most model trains require

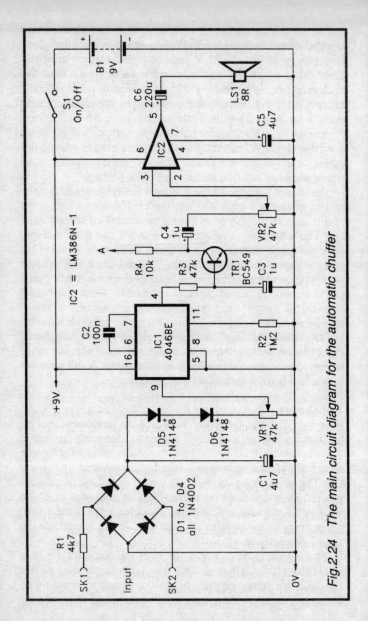

Fig.2.24 The main circuit diagram for the automatic chuffer

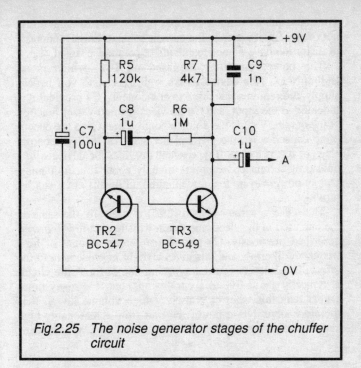

Fig.2.25 The noise generator stages of the chuffer circuit

a fair voltage before they start to move. The voltage drop through the bridge rectifier plus the control characteristic of the v.c.o. itself help to prevent the v.c.o. from starting at too low a track voltage, but the further voltage drop through D5 and D6 is needed in order to give the circuit a suitably large starting voltage.

IC1 provides a high quality squarewave signal, and this is coupled to the input of the v.c.a. via a simple lowpass filter comprised of R3 and C3. The filtering rounds the waveform slightly, giving a less abrupt attack and decay to the bursts of noise. This gives a slightly better effect than using the raw squarewave signal. The v.c.a. is a very simple type using TR1 and R4. The noise signal is allowed to pass through R4 and on to the power amplifier with little attenuation when TR1 is switched off. When TR1 is switched on it provides a very low collector-to-emitter resistance, and large losses through R4.

The audio quality of such a simple v.c.a. is very low, but this is not of any significance in the current context. Large amounts of distortion have no noticeable affect on a noise signal.

The power amplifier is based on IC2, which is an LM386N-1. This device works well on a nine volt battery supply and requires few discrete components. C4 provides d.c. blocking at the input, and C6 provides the equivalent function at the output. VR2 is the volume control, and C5 is the decoupling capacitor for the preamplifier stage of IC2. The output stage of IC2 is a class B type which provides the device with a quiescent current consumption of only about four milliamps. Output powers of up to a few hundred milliwatts r.m.s. can be provided.

The noise generator (Figure 2.25) is basically the same as the one used in the electronic steam whistle circuit which was described previously. C9 provides a certain amount of high frequency filtering, and this gives a slight improvement to the effect. The quiescent current consumption of the entire circuit is typically about five to six milliamps, but it is many times higher than this when it is used at high volume levels. It is therefore advisable to power the unit from a reasonably high capacity battery, such as six HP7 size cells in a plastic holder.

Construction

Figure 2.26 shows the component layout and wiring for the automatic train chuffer. The underside view of the board is provided in Figure 2.27. The board measures 51 holes by 22 copper strips. This device is rather more complex than those described previously, and a little extra care is therefore needed when constructing it. This project is less than ideal for complete beginners at electronic project construction. Note that IC1 is a CMOS device, and that it requires the normal anti-static handling precautions.

When initially testing the completed project, start with VR1 at a roughly mid-point setting. The unit should then work quite well, but some further adjustment of VR1 will probably be needed in order to get the start-up voltages of the train and the chuffer unit reasonably well synchronised. This is just a matter of trial and error.

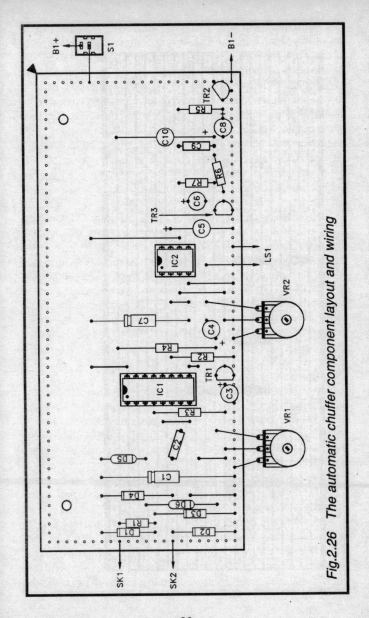

Fig.2.26 The automatic chuffer component layout and wiring

99

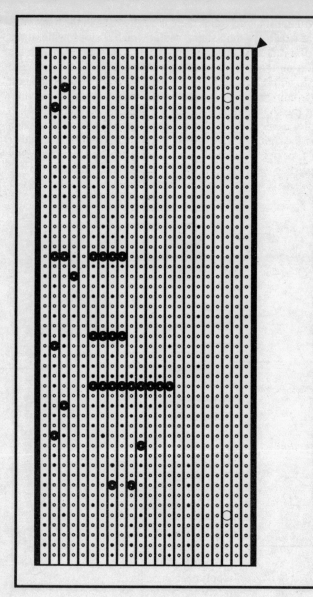

Fig.2.27   The underside view of the automatic chuffer board

With most model trains there is a difference in the track voltage at which the train starts, and at which it stops again at the end of a run. This makes it impossible to accurately match the chuffer unit to both the starting and stopping of the train. You have to adjust VR1 for what you subjectively rate to be the best compromise setting. I generally find results are most convincing if the sound effect is accurately matched to the train when it pulls away, even if this gives a relatively large mismatch when the train comes to a halt. A normal potentiometer rather than a preset is used for VR1 so that the unit can be easily adjusted to suit different locomotives, and variations in the rolling stock used with each locomotive.

Components for Figures 2.24 and 2.25

Resistors (all 0.25 watt 5% carbon film)
R1	4k7
R2	1M2
R3	47k
R4	10k
R5	120k
R6	1M
R7	4k7

Potentiometers
VR1	47k lin carbon
VR2	47k log carbon

Capacitors
C1	4µ7 50V axial elect
C2	100n polyester
C3	1µ 50V radial elect
C4	1µ 50V radial elect
C5	4µ7 50V radial elect
C6	220µ 10V radial elect
C7	100µ 10V axial elect
C8	1µ 50V radial elect
C9	1n polyester
C10	1µ 50V radial elect

Semiconductors

IC1	4046BE
IC2	LM386N-1
TR1	BC549
TR2	BC547
TR3	BC549
D1 to D4	1N4002 (4 off)
D5	1N4148
D6	1N4148

Miscellaneous

S1	s.p.s.t. min toggle switch
B1	9 volt (6 HP7 size cells in holder)
LS1	miniature 8R loudspeaker
SK1	4mm socket or terminal post
SK2	4mm socket or terminal post

Case, 0.1 inch matrix stripboard having 51 holes by 22 copper strips, battery connector (PP3 type), control knob (2 off), 16-pin d.i.l. holder, 8-pin d.i.l. holder, multi-strand connecting wire, solder, etc.

Manual Chuffer

If a chuffer unit having manual control of the chuff rate is required, it is basically just a matter of omitting some of the components in the automatic chuffer circuit. Figure 2.28 shows the main circuit for a manual version of the automatic chuffer. The noise generator is exactly the same as in the original unit (i.e. the same as Figure 2.25). The bridge rectifier, the lowpass filter, and the two diodes have been removed from the original circuit, and the top end of VR1 is connected to the +9 volt supply. The output frequency of IC1, and therefore the chuff rate as well, is controlled by the setting of VR1.

The modified component layout and wiring for the manual version of the chuffer are provided in Figure 2.29. The underside view of the circuit board is shown in Figure 2.30. The board is slightly smaller than the one used in the automatic chuffer, and it actually measures 46 holes by 22 copper strips.

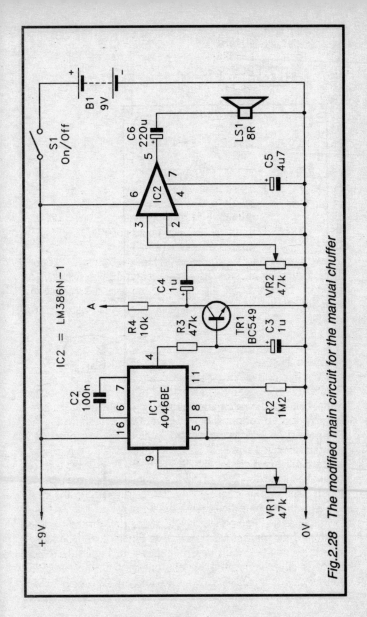

Fig.2.28 The modified main circuit for the manual chuffer

103

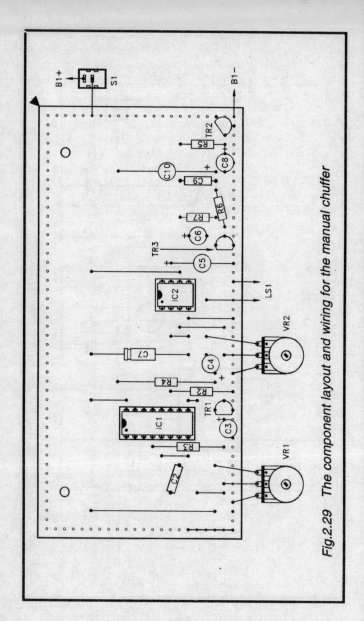

Fig.2.29   The component layout and wiring for the manual chuffer

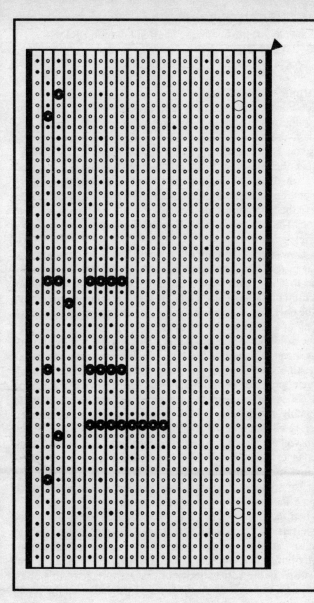

Fig.2.30   The underside view of the manual chuffer board

105

Components for Figures 2.25 and 2.28
The same as for the automatic chuffer, but omit SK1, SK2, D1 to D6, R1, and C1.

Electronic Track "Cleaner"

Model trains, even when used with a good controller, often provide rather unreliable results when used at slow speeds. The problem seems to be caused by small amounts of dirt and grease on the track which can produce a bad electrical contact between the track and the locomotive. When the train is travelling at medium and high speeds there is normally no major problem, because the momentum of the train will usually take it past the contaminated section of track and onto a clean section. The train may falter slightly, but it will not come to a complete standstill.

At slow speeds the train often lacks sufficient momentum to take it beyond the dirty section of track, and the train simply comes to a halt. With the electric motor out of electrical contact with the controller, the quality of the controller is irrelevant, and the only way of starting the train again is to manually move it along to a clean section of track.

One solution to the problem is to keep the tracks scrupulously clean, although it can be difficult to maintain the tracks in pristine condition in the long term. An electronic track "cleaner" provides an alternative solution. A device of this type does not actually clean the tracks at all, and it could more reasonably regarded as a dirt "zapper" than a track cleaner. Basically all that an electronic track "cleaner" does is to place a high voltage signal across the tracks. This signal is at a high impedance, and under normal circumstances it is virtually short circuited by the low impedance of the electric motor in the train. This reduces the voltage to an insignificant level which has no affect on the operation of the train.

When the train reaches a dirty section of track, the motor loses electrical contact with the track. The motor then fails to place any loading on the high voltage signal, which consequently jumps to its normal level. This is typically about 150 to 200 volts. In the vast majority of cases a voltage of this order is sufficient to break down the layer of insulation on the track,

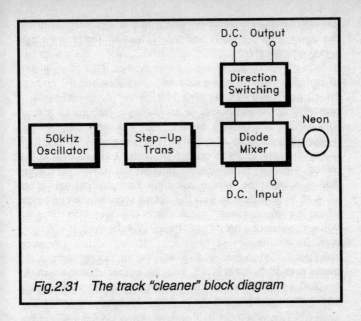

Fig.2.31 The track "cleaner" block diagram

placing the motor back in contact with the track. The controller and the high voltage source are then placed back in contact with the electric motor. The high voltage source is then loaded down to a low potential once more, and the controller supplies power to the motor. In practice this process is usually repeated a number of times in rapid succession until the locomotive has cleared the dirty stretch of track.

Having a high voltage across the track might seem to be dangerous, but it has to be borne in mind that this voltage is at a high impedance. Only a very low current is available, and even drawing a current of a few hundred microamps loads the voltage down to a relatively low level. It is advisable to avoid contact with any high voltage source, but it is highly unlikely that this equipment could provide even a moderate electric shock.

The block diagram of Figure 2.31 helps to explain the basic way in which the electronic track "cleaner" functions. On the face of it, the 230 volt a.c. mains supply could be used to provide the high voltage required to "zap" the dirt. However,

107

this approach has a major drawback in that it is difficult to use the mains supply directly and safely. Instead, the high voltage signal is derived from a low voltage d.c. supply via a high frequency oscillator and a step-up transformer. This gives plenty of isolation between the tracks and the mains supply, and the circuit that generates the high voltage supply is incapable of providing an output power of more than a fraction of a watt. This method is relatively complex, but it is very safe.

For this system to work properly it is essential that the high voltage supply and the output from the train controller are mixed together in a suitable manner. It is of paramount importance that the high voltage from the track "cleaner" is not allowed to find its way into the output stage of the controller, where it could obviously cause costly damage. Also, the high voltage source can only "zap" the dirt on the track if there is a high impedance across the tracks. Under normal operating conditions the controller will still be connected across the tracks even if the train is not. The low output impedance of the controller would load down the output signal from the step-up transformer, and prevent the system from operating properly.

In order to obtain the required mixing of the two signals it is merely necessary to use a simple diode mixer. One problem in doing this is that the mixer only works properly if the input voltage from the controller has the right polarity. A direction control switch is therefore included at the output of the track "cleaner", and the controller's direction switch is left unused. A neon indicator at the output of the unit switches on when a high voltage is present, and it therefore flashes on when the track "cleaner" is "doing the business".

The Circuit

The full circuit diagram for the electronic track "cleaner" is shown in Figure 2.32. It is based on IC1, which is a 555 timer used in the standard astable (oscillator) mode. In theory, timing components C2, R1, and R2 set the output frequency at around 60 to 70kHz, but in practice the typical output frequency seems to be somewhat lower at a little over 50kHz. Step-up transformer T1 has a ferrite potcore which gives good efficiency at this frequency. C3 couples the output of IC1 to the primary winding of T1, and R3 limits the drive current to T1. This is

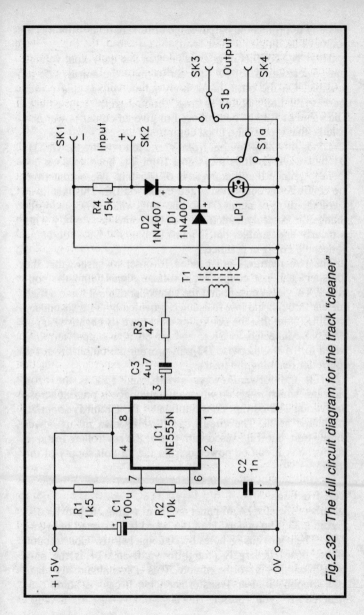

Fig.2.32 The full circuit diagram for the track "cleaner"

109

partially to protect the output stage of IC1, but it also limits the output of the unit to a safer level.

There is a conflict of interest here, in that the output voltage and power should be low in order to make the unit as safe as possible. On the other hand, high output voltage and power increase the unit's ability to "zap" dirt and grease on the track. The value of R3 has been chosen to give an output power and voltage that represent a good compromise.

The high voltage output from T1 is fed to the tracks via D1. D1 half-wave rectifies the signal from T1, but this does not seem to reduce the effectiveness of the unit. The output from the controller is connected to the tracks via D2. This results in a voltage drop of about 0.6 to one volt, which will obviously change the control characteristic of the controller slightly. This is clearly undesirable, but is unavoidable, and has little or no noticeable effect in practice.

The two rectifiers are needed in order to ensure that the "cleaner" can not couple high voltage signals into the controller. They also ensure that the controller can not force a high current through the low resistance provided by T1's secondary winding. Note that the controller must have its negative output terminal connected to SK1, and its positive output terminal wired to SK2. Otherwise D2 will prevent the output from the controller reaching the tracks.

S1 is the forward/reverse switch, and LP1 is the neon indicator which lights up when a high voltage is present across the tracks. The current consumption of the circuit is about 20 milliamps or so. The circuit can have its own mains power supply unit, but if it is used with one of the controllers featured in this book it can be powered from the 15 volt supply of the controller.

Construction

Details of the stripboard panel and hard wiring are provided in Figure 2.33. The underside of the board is illustrated in Figure 2.34. The board has 38 holes by 20 copper strips. Construction of the board is largely straightforward, and T1 is the only component that is worthy of note. This is available ready-made as a Maplin "Ioniser Transformer", but it can be home constructed if you prefer. It is wound on an LA4343

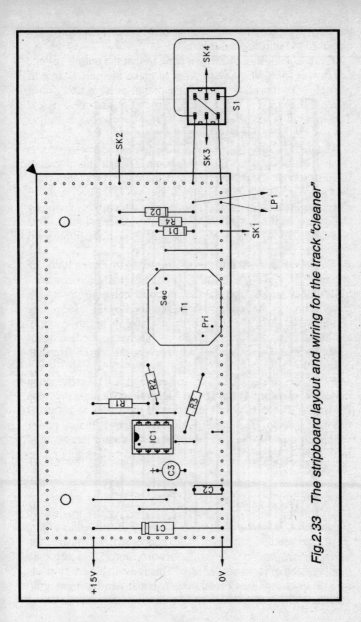

Fig.2.33   The stripboard layout and wiring for the track "cleaner"

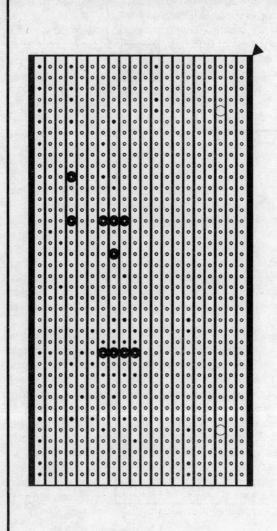

Fig.2.34 The underside view of the track "cleaner" board

112

pot core (or similar). Note that you will need a bobbin and a pair of metal clips in addition to the pot core, and that these are normally sold as separate items.

The primary winding connects to one pair of pins, and it consists of 10 turns of 0.56 millimetre (or 24 s.w.g.) enamelled copper wire. The secondary connects to the other pair of pins, and it consists 600 turns of 0.125 millimetre (or 40 s.w.g.) enamelled copper wire. The secondary must be wound reasonably neatly or the winding might be too large, preventing the bobbin from fitting into the two halves of the pot core. The pair of metal clips are used to hold the two halves of the core together. It is obviously essential to fit T1 to the board the right way round so that it provides a voltage step-up and not a step-down. On the ready-made version the secondary side of the component is identified by an extra pin. This pin does not connect to either winding of the component incidentally.

There should be no difficulty in completing the small amount of hard wiring. LP1 must be a type that has an integral series resistor for use with the 230 volt a.c. mains supply. An ordinary neon bulb is only suitable if it is provided with an external series resistor of about 270k in value. The unit can handle output currents of up to about one amp. Currents of up to about 2 amps or so can be accommodated if a 1N5408 is used for D2.

As pointed out earlier, the unit will not work properly unless the controller is connected to SK1 and SK2 with the correct polarity. If necessary, the correct polarity can be found by trial and error. If the output of the controller is not coupled through to the tracks, the polarity is wrong! LP1 should light up continuously with no train on the tracks, but it will be at something less than normal brightness. LP1 should switch off with the train in position on the tracks, but it will flash intermittently with the train moving (unless the tracks are "squeaky clean").

Although the output from the unit is unlikely to inflict a significant electric shock, it may well provide a noticeable shock. High voltages should always be treated with respect, and it is always best to avoid contact with any high voltages.

Components for Figure 2.31

Resistors (0.25 watt 5% carbon film except where noted)
R1   1k5
R2   10k
R3   47R 1 watt
R4   15k

Capacitors
C1   100µ 16V axial elect
C2   1n polyester
C3   4µ7 50V radial elect

Semiconductors
IC1   NE555N
D1   1N4007
D2   1N4007

Miscellaneous
T1   see text
S1   d.p.d.t. toggle switch
LP1   Neon indicator having integral series resistor
            for 230 volt a.c. mains use
SK1 to SK4 4mm socket or terminal post (4 off)
Case, 0.1 inch stripboard having 38 holes by 20 copper strips,
8-pin d.i.l. holder, multi-strand connecting wire, solder, etc.

Chapter 3

COMPUTERISED LAYOUTS

This chapter is really only intended for those readers who are reasonably experienced at electronic project construction, and also understand the fundamentals of computer interfacing and BASIC programming. The subject of this chapter is using an IBM PC or PC compatible computer to control a model railway. The PCs and compatibles have been chosen as they are the nearest thing to a standard computer, and are now far more popular than any other computer. Much of the material is actually of a general nature, and could be applied equally well to other computers, but the circuits have only been tested with IBM compatible PCs. Obviously the programs are specific to PCs, and would need a fair amount of modification in order to run properly on other computers.

Ins and Outs

There is insufficient space available here for a detailed explanation of computer interfacing in general, or even an in-depth account of interfacing PCs to the outside world. However, we will briefly consider the method of PC interfacing used for the circuits featured in this chapter. The circuits are interfaced to the PC via one of its parallel printer ports, and they will work equally well using port 1 (LPT1) or port 2 (LPT2).

Using a printer port has an obvious drawback in that there are only a rather limited number of input and output lines available. The advantage of this system is that all PCs are normally supplied complete with at least one printer port. In many cases the computer will only be supplied with one printer port. This port is likely to be used for its intended purpose, but it only requires the addition of an inexpensive expansion card to provide a second printer port. The alternative is to use a switching device (called a "printer sharer") to enable one printer port to be switched between use as a printer port, and a general purpose port for use with your add-ons. A card to provide a second port is the more convenient method, and may well be cheaper.

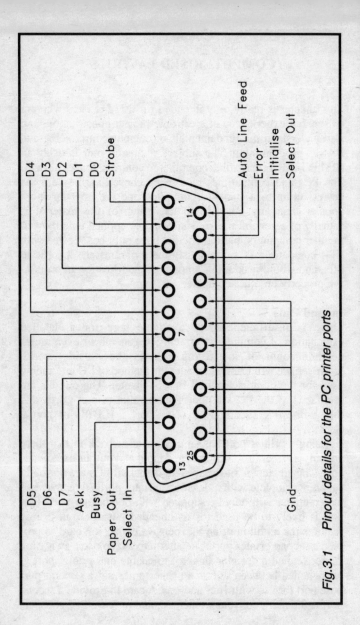

Fig.3.1   Pinout details for the PC printer ports

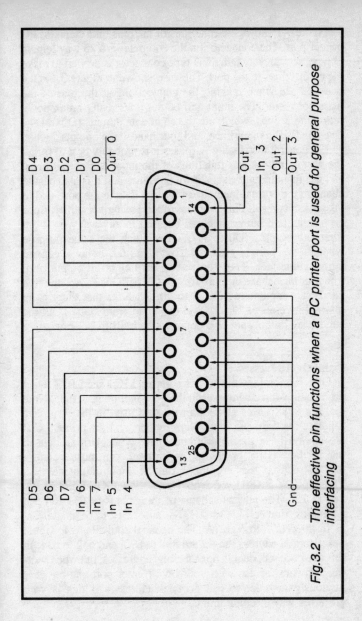

Fig.3.2   The effective pin functions when a PC printer port is used for general purpose interfacing

117

Figure 3.1 shows the functions of the pins on a standard PC printer port. The connector on the computer is a 25 way female D type, so a 25 way female D type connector is needed to make the connections to the port. The view shown in Figure 3.1 is the one you see when making the connections at the rear of the male connector. The input and output lines really break down into three groups, which are the eight data outputs (D0 to D7), five handshake input lines, and four handshake outputs.

For general interfacing purposes it is probably best to forget the normal names and functions of the input and output lines, and use the alternative set shown in Figure 3.2. It is also best to abandon the normal methods of writing data to the port, and to take direct control. This provides much greater versatility, since each input and output line can be used in any way you wish. The data outputs (D0 to D7) serve much the same purpose whether the port is used to drive a printer, or as a general purpose interface. They form a standard eight-bit output port. The four handshake outputs are "Out 0" to "Out 3", and the five handshake inputs are "IN 3" to "In 7". Note that there is an internal inverter on "In 7", and that apart from "Out 2" all the handshake outputs are also obtained via built-in inverters.

Properly Addressed

In DOS terminology the printer ports are LPT1 and LPT2. They each occupy three addresses in the PC's input/output map. Note that the 8088 series of microprocessors used in the PCs have separate memory and input/output maps, and the printer ports are obviously in the input/output map. When writing data to one of these ports, or reading from them, you must therefore use instructions that are appropriate to input/output devices. Thus, in GW BASIC you would use INP and OUT, not PEEK and POKE. The normal scheme of things is for LPT1 to be at addresses from &H378 to &H37A, and LPT2 to be at addresses from &H278 to &H27A. The decimal equivalents for these hexadecimal address ranges are 888 to 890, and 632 to 634. In this book we will deal in hexadecimal addresses, but when writing software for use with your own printer port add-ons it is obviously in order to use decimal addresses if this is your preferred way of doing things.

This table shows the location of each printer port input/output line in the PC's input/output map.

I/O Line Address Mapping

LPT2
&H278

Bit	Line
0	D0
1	D1
2	D2
3	D3
4	D4
5	D5
6	D6
7	D7

&H279

Bit	Line
0	unused
1	unused
2	unused
3	In 3
4	In 4
5	In 5
6	In 6
7	In 7 (inverted)

&H27A

Bit	Line
0	Out 0 (inverted)
1	Out 1 (inverted)
2	Out 2
3	Out 3 (inverted)
4	unused
5	unused
6	unused
7	unused

LPT1
&H378

Bit	Line
0	D0
1	D1
2	D2
3	D3
4	D4
5	D5
6	D6
7	D7

&H379

Bit	Line
0	unused
1	unused
2	unused
3	In 3
4	In 4
5	In 5
6	In 6
7	In 7 (inverted)

&H37A

Bit	Line
0	Out 0 (inverted)
1	Out 1 (inverted)
2	Out 2
3	Out 3 (inverted)
4	unused
5	unused
6	unused
7	unused

Writing to the eight data lines of either port is very straight-forward, and it is just a matter writing the correct value to the appropriate address. For example, to set all eight data lines of LPT2 high a value of 255 would be written to address &H278. In GW BASIC or Q BASIC this would achieved using the OUT instruction (i.e. OUT &H278,255). There is no need to include data latches in your add-on circuits, because the data outputs are latching types.

Presumably due to the fact that some commercial peripherals for PCs use the printer port for bidirectional parallel interfacing, some people seem to have gained the impression that the data lines can be used as inputs or outputs. Unfortunately, this can only be achieved using a special type of printer port, and it is not possible using a standard PC printer port. The hardware that provides the eight data lines can only provide outputs, and none of these lines can be used as inputs. Parallel data can only be input via the printer port using slightly circuitous methods. Fortunately, for many model railway applications a few input lines are perfectly adequate.

Like the data outputs, the four handshake outputs at addresses &H27A and &H37A are latching types, and they can only act as outputs. Again, it is just a matter of writing the appropriate value to the port address. With handshake lines it would usually be easier if they could be operated entirely independently. This is clearly not possible here, because all four handshake outputs of each printer port are at the same address. Therefore, when altering the state of one output, great care must be taken not to alter the states of the other three outputs.

A standard way of achieving this is to read from the port to determine the states of the outputs, and then work out a modified value to write back to the port, so that only the desired change is made. This is not a reliable method in this case, since this is a write-only address. You can not be sure that the values read back will accurately reflect the states of the outputs. In fact it is highly unlikely that they would, and with most printer port cards a value of 255 will always be returned from the handshake output address. This is simply because no hardware is actually activated by a read operation to the handshake output addresses, and the data lines of the microprocessor are left free to drift. They all drift to the high state, giving a returned value of 255. Where necessary, your software routines must therefore be carefully written so that the program "remembers" the last value written to the handshake outputs.

Of course, with only four of the bits at each of these addresses actually used, only data values from 0 to 15 are valid. Values from 16 to 255 will not cause a software error, but only the least significant four bits of these values will affect the states of the handshake outputs. For instance, a value of 16 would set all four outputs low, and a value of 255 would set them all high. On the other hand, it would not be good programming practice to write out-of-range values to a port.

Position Sensing
The computer can simply be used as the basis of an otherwise fairly conventional model train controller, or it can be used to provide fully automatic control. Another approach is to have manual control of the train or trains, but with the computer controlling the signals. With both types of control it is often necessary to have some form of feedback from the layout to the computer, so that the computer knows when the train passes certain positions on the track. This is normally handled in much the same way as when position sensing is needed by a non-computerised control system, with reed or micro-switches being used to detect the passing train.

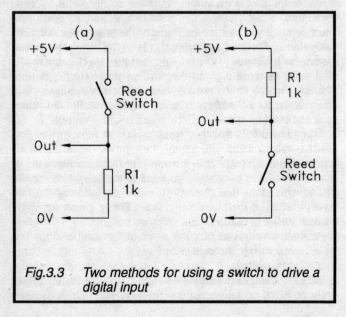

Fig.3.3   Two methods for using a switch to drive a digital input

Figure 3.3 shows the two basic methods of using a reed switch (or any other mechanical switch) to drive a digital input of a computer. The difference between the two is that the output of (a) is normally low and goes high when the switch is activated, while the output of (b) is normally high and goes low when the switch is activated. In a computer application it does not normally matter which method of connection is used, as the software can be written to suit either method. My preference is for the method shown in (a), as it is easier to think in terms of a returned value of 0 as the standby state, and a returned value of one, two, etc., as the active state.

Although this type of sensor may seem to be so simple that nothing could go wrong, in practice there are a few potential problems. Mechanical switches are notoriously noisy, and often suffer from a certain amount of contact bounce. This results in a series of brief pulses being produced each time the switch opens or closes, rather than single "clean" transitions being produced.

The importance of this (or the lack of it) depends on whether or not the switch circuit feeds into an edge triggered input. If it does, there is a real danger of multiple triggering occurring. There are software solutions, the most simple of which is to have a time delay so that once a trigger signal has been detected, no others are serviced for a short period of time. Hardware solutions are more popular though, and are extremely simple. The basic technique is to use a pulse stretcher which holds the output in the active state for a short while once an initial trigger pulse has been received.

This technique can also be of benefit if the switch circuit is used to drive an ordinary (non-edge triggered) digital input. If only momentary operation of the switch will be produced (as it will in the current context), it is possible that the software routine which monitors the input port will sometimes miss the input pulses. The likelihood of this depends on how frequently the monitoring routine will test the input lines, but using a pulse stretcher to give pulses of (say) about one second in duration should ensure that there is absolutely no possibility of any pulses being missed.

Figure 3.4 shows the circuit diagram for a very simple pulse stretcher based on a trigger/inverter stage. The latter is one of

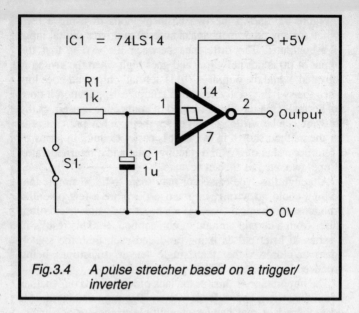

Fig.3.4   A pulse stretcher based on a trigger/inverter

the six trigger/inverters in a 74LS14. This does not provide a particularly long output pulse, but it is usually sufficient to provide effective de-bouncing. It is very economic since six resistors, six capacitors, and one 74LS14 will provide half a dozen de-bounce circuits.

For a longer output pulse duration the basic 555 monostable circuit of Figure 3.5 can be used. R2 and C1 are the timing components, and the pulse duration is equal to 1.1 C R seconds (where C is the timing capacitor value in microfarads, and R is the timing resistance in megohms). The specified values give a pulse duration of about 1.1 seconds, but using larger timing component values it is possible to obtain pulse durations of several seconds if necessary.

Signals

Driving LEDs by signals from a computer does not require much in the way of additional hardware. In many cases it is possible to drive a LED direct from a digital output, but via a current limiting resistor of around 390 ohms in value. The only

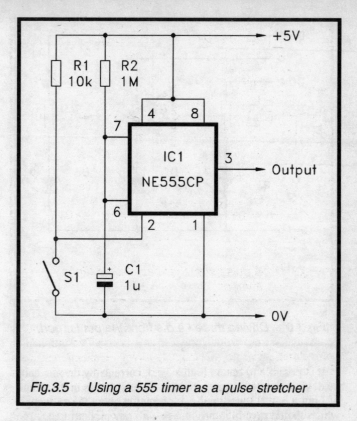

Fig.3.5   Using a 555 timer as a pulse stretcher

slight problem is that not all digital outputs can provide a high
enough current to give good l.e.d. brightness. Some component
suppliers now offer l.e.d.s that are designed to provide good
brightness when operated at low currents of around 2 milliamps, and this offers a possible solution.

Figure 3.6 shows a simple circuit that provides three aspect
signalling. This simply drives the three signal l.e.d.s from lines
D0 to D2 of the printer port. The "red", "amber", and "green"
signals are selected by writing values of 1, 2, and 4 (respectively) to the printer port. The "amber" signal can be provided
by an orange or yellow l.e.d., but to my eyes yellow l.e.d.s look
marginally closer to the colour of the "real thing."

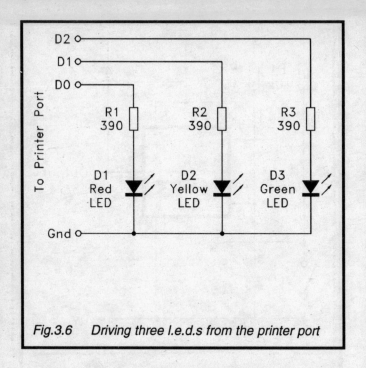

Fig.3.6   Driving three l.e.d.s from the printer port

It is possible to obtain higher l.e.d. currents by driving each l.e.d. via a simple common emitter driver stage, as in the circuit of Figure 3.7. R3 sets the l.e.d. current at about 20 milliamps, which should give high brightness with any modern LED. The circuit can be used to drive miniature filament bulbs if an appropriate supply voltage is used and the R3 is replaced with a shorting link. The bulb should have a voltage rating of no more than 24 volts, and a current rating of no more than about 100 milliamps or so.

This GW BASIC program provides a simple form of automatic signalling, with the signal repeatedly going through a "green" – "red" – "amber" – "green" sequence. Manual override is also available. Pressing the "g", "r", and "a" keys respectively set the signal to "green", "red", and "amber." Pressing the "s" key stops the program and returns the system to the direct mode.

126

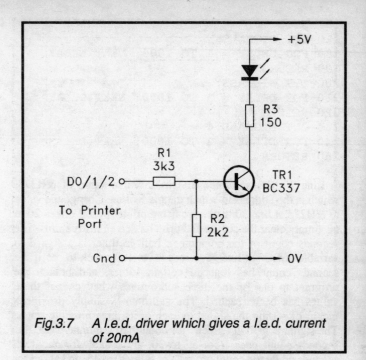

Fig.3.7   A l.e.d. driver which gives a l.e.d. current of 20mA

```
10   REM Simple automatic signal program
20   CLS
30   SIGNALS = &H378
35   PRINT "Press 's' key to stop program"
40   PRINT "Press 'g' key for green"
50   PRINT "Press 'a' key for amber"
60   PRINT "Press 'r' key for red"
70   SEC = VAL(MID$(TIME$,7,2))
80   IF SEC = 30 THEN GOSUB 170
90   IF SEC = 45 THEN GOSUB 200
100  IF SEC = 59 THEN GOSUB 230
110  A$ = INKEY$
120  IF A$ = "s" THEN END
130  IF A$ = "r" THEN GOSUB 170
140  IF A$ = "a" THEN GOSUB 200
150  IF A$ = "g" THEN GOSUB 230
```

```
160 GOTO 70
170 OUT SIGNALS,1
180 FOR DELAY = 1 TO 1000: NEXT DELAY
190 RETURN
200 OUT SIGNALS, 2
210 FOR DELAY = 1 TO 1000: NEXT DELAY
220 RETURN
230 OUT SIGNALS,4
240 FOR DELAY = 1 TO 1000: NEXT DELAY
250 RETURN
```

Line 30 sets variable "SIGNALS" at a value of &H378, which is the address to which data is written. Change the value to &H278 at line 30 if you are using printer port 2. Lines 20 to 60 simply clear the screen and print on-screen instructions. The seconds count of the computer's built-in timer is assigned to variable "SEC" at line 70. Lines 80 to 100 check to see if the seconds count has reached certain values, and branch the program to one of the three subroutines when one of these values has been reached. The subroutines simply provide a means of setting the signal to each of its three possible states. The signal is held at "green" for about half a minute while the seconds count goes from 59 to 30, at "amber" for about 15 seconds while the count progresses from 30 to 45, and at red for about 15 seconds while the count goes from 45 to 59.

At lines 110 to 150 the keyboard is read, and checks are made to see if the "s", "a", "g", or "r" key has been pressed. The program is brought to an end if the "s" key has been pressed, or branched to the appropriate subroutine if one of the other three keys has been operated. The GOTO at line 160 continuously loops the program around lines 70 to 160.

This next listing is for an automatic signal that mimics a real signalling system. Many "real world" train signalling systems have a sensor by the signal, and the signal is automatically set to "red" as a train passes by. A sensor further along the track sets the signal to "amber" as the train passes over it, and a third sensor, yet further along the track, automatically sets the signal to "green" as the train passes by. The purpose of this system is to ensure that there is always a certain minimum distance between trains, and the possibility of one train running into the back of another is avoided. Of course, the signalman can manually override the signals if the need should arise.

This signalling system provides the same basic function, with reed or micro-switches being used to detect the passing train. The keyboard provides manual override. The signal lights are driven from D0 to D2 of the printer port, as in the previous signalling system. The reed or micro switches drive "In 4", "In 5", and "In 6" via pulse stretchers. I used 555 timers to provide the pulse stretching (Figure 3.8). S1 is the sensor near the signal, S2 is the sensor switch further along the track, and S3 is the sensor positioned furthest from the signal.

```
10    REM Automatic signal program
20    CLS
30    PRINT "press 's' key to end program"
40    PRINT "Press 'r' key for red"
50    PRINT "Press 'a' key for amber"
60    PRINT "press 'g' key for green"
70    SIGNALS = &H378
80    SWITCHES = &H379
90    OUT SIGNALS,4
100   IF (INP(SWITCHES) AND 16) = 16 THEN
      GOSUB 190
110   IF (INP(SWITCHES) AND 32) = 32 THEN
      GOSUB 210
120   IF (INP(SWITCHES) AND 64) = 64 THEN
      GOSUB 230
130   A$ = INKEY$
140   IF A$ = "s" THEN END
150   IF A$ = "r" THEN OUT SIGNALS,1
160   IF A$ = "a" THEN OUT SIGNALS,2
170   IF A$ = "g" THEN OUT SIGNALS,4
180   GOTO 100
190   OUT SIGNALS,1
200   RETURN
210   OUT SIGNALS,2
220   RETURN
230   OUT SIGNALS,4
240   RETURN
```

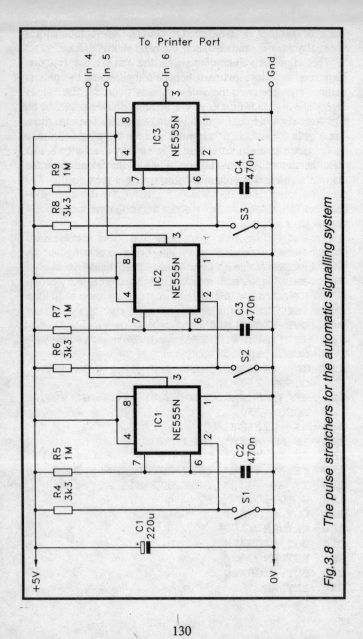

Fig.3.8   The pulse stretchers for the automatic signalling system

130

Lines 20 to 60 clear the screen and print on-screen instructions. Lines 70 and 80 set variables "SIGNALS" and "SWITCHES" at values of &H378 and &H379 respectively. These are the addresses to which data for the signal lights is written, and data from the sensor switches is read. Use values of &H278 and &H279 if you are using printer port 2. The signal is set at its initial "green" state at line 90. The next three lines check the sensor switches, and branch the program to one of the three subroutines if a switch has been activated. The selected subroutines sets the signal to the appropriate state for the sensor switch that has been activated. Lines 130 to 170 provide manual control of the signal, again via the three subroutines. Line 180 simply loops the program indefinitely around lines 100 to 170.

These signalling systems can obviously be simplified to provide two aspect signalling, or extended to accommodate the four aspect variety (with twin amber signal lights). It should also be possible to add facilities. For example, the second system could be made to hold the signal at red for a certain time on every "nth" lap of the layout. An advantage of a computer based system is that it is often possible to implement additional features by modifying the software, with no extra hardware being needed. There is certainly plenty of room for experimentation with these signalling systems.

Components for Figures 3.6 and 3.8

Resistors (all 0.25 watt 5% carbon film)

R1	390R
R2	390R
R3	390R
R4	3k3
R5	1M
R6	3k3
R7	1M
R8	3k3
R9	1M

Capacitors

C1	220μ 10V elect

C2	470n polyester
C3	470n polyester
C4	470n polyester

Semiconductors

IC1	NE555N
IC2	NE555N
IC3	NE555N
D1	Red l.e.d.
D2	Yellow or orange l.e.d.
D3	Green l.e.d.

Miscellaneous

| S1 to S3 | Micro or reed switches (3 off) |

Case, circuit board, 8-pin d.i.l. holder (3 off), 25 way male D type connector and 7 way lead, multi-strand connecting wire, etc.

Train Controllers

Control of a small d.c. electric motor from a computer via a digital to analogue converter is a simple process. It basically just requires some voltage amplification and some high current buffering at the output of the converter. The controller circuits featured here are designed to provide a maximum output potential of 12 volts or so at currents of up to one amp. The larger gauge model trains sometimes require a supply current of up to about 2 amps, and these circuits can handle the extra current provided adequate heatsinking is provided for the output transistor, and the power supply circuit has an adequate rating. Note that these circuits require their own mains power supply units, and they can not be powered from the PC's supply rails. The mains power supply circuit featured in chapter one (Figure 1.4) is suitable for use with these controller circuits.

Figures 3.9 and 3.10 show the circuit diagram for a controller of the constant voltage variety. This is a computer equivalent to the manual constant voltage controller featured in Chapter 1. The circuit of Figure 3.9 is for the digital to analogue converter. This is a simple but high quality eight-bit converter circuit based on the ZN426E. This converter has a built-in

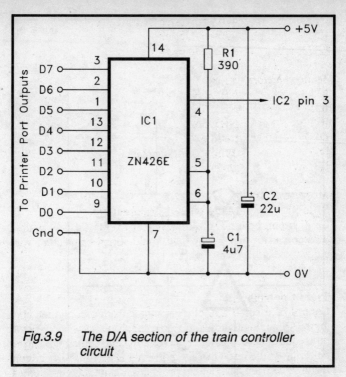

Fig.3.9 *The D/A section of the train controller circuit*

voltage reference, but it requires discrete load resistor R1 and decoupling capacitor C1. The output voltage range of the converter is from 0 to 2.55 volts, and only a very modest output current is available.

The amplifier circuit of Figure 3.10 is therefore used to provide a small amount of voltage gain and a large amount of current amplification. The controller circuit must provide a voltage amplification of just under five times in order to convert the 0 to 2.55 volts from the converter into the required 0 to 12 volt output range. IC2 is an operational amplifier used in the non-inverting mode, and this stage provides the voltage amplification. R2, R3, and VR1 are the negative feedback circuit which sets the voltage gain at the correct level. VR1 must be adjusted to give precisely the required gain of 4.7 times. In practice, the converter is fed with a value of 255 in order to set the maximum

133

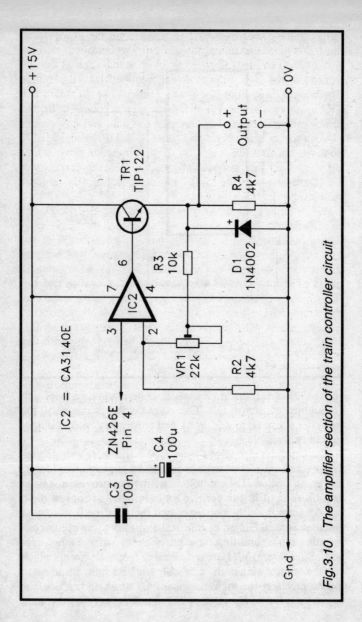

Fig.3.10 The amplifier section of the train controller circuit

output voltage, and then VR1 is adjusted for the lowest resistance that gives maximum output from the controller.

TR1 is an emitter follower output stage that enables the unit to provide the high output currents required by a d.c. motor. The current drive from IC2 is quite limited, which means that TR1 must provide a very high current gain. A power Darlington device is therefore used in the TR1 position, and this gives a current gain of a few thousand times. The TIP121 and TIP122 both work well in this circuit. D1 is a protection diode which suppresses any high reverse voltage spikes that might otherwise be generated across the highly inductive load. R4 is simply a load resistor for TR1.

When building the unit remember that the CA3140E used for IC1 has a PMOS input stage, and that it consequently requires the standard anti-static handling precautions. TR1 has to dissipate several watts at most output voltages, which means that it must be fitted on a substantial heatsink. One having a rating of about 5 degrees celsius per watt (or less) should suffice for output currents of up to 1 amp. For a 2 amp version of the circuit a heatsink with a rating of no more than about 2.5 degrees celsius per watt should be used. The heat-tab of TR1 connects internally to the collector terminal, which means that it will be necessary to insulate TR1 from the heatsink using a T0-220 insulating kit.

In use you will almost certainly find that there is quite a wide range of low values that fail to operate the motor. This is simply because most d.c. electric motors, especially when heavily loaded, require three or four volts before they will start to turn. In some applications it might be necessary to allow for this in the software, with low output values (apart from 0 for "off") being avoided. Although the motor's speed is not continuously variable and it actually has what is likely to be around 200 different speeds, it is unlikely that there will be any obvious change in speed from one control value to the next. This gives what is effectively a continuously variable speed.

Components for Figures 3.9 and 3.10

Resistors (all 0.25 watt 5% carbon film)
R1   390

R2	4k7
R3	10k
R4	4k7

Potentiometer

| VR1 | 22k miniature preset |

Capacitors

C1	4µ7 63V elect
C2	22µ 16V elect
C3	100n ceramic
C4	100µ 25V elect

Semiconductors

IC1	ZN426E
IC2	CA3140E
TR1	TIP121 or TIP122
D1	1N4002

Miscellaneous

8 pin d.i.l. holder
14 pin d.i.l. holder
25 way D plug and lead
Heatsink for TR1 (see text)
Case, circuit board, solder, etc.

Forward/Reverse

As pointed out in chapter one, the direction of a d.c. electric
motor is controlled by the polarity of the applied voltage. This
application obviously demands some form of direction control
via the computer. Basically all that is needed is a relay driver
and a relay having twin changeover contacts. The latter are
wired in the manner shown in Figure 3.11. The contacts must
be of the break before make variety, and not the make before
break type (which would short circuit the output of the controller on each changeover). All the relays I have ever used have
been equipped with break before make contacts, but it is
worthwhile checking this point just in case. Manual direction
switching may be adequate, and this depends on how much or

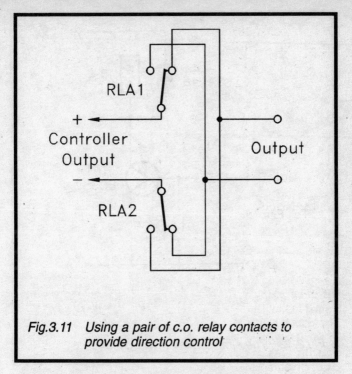

Fig.3.11 Using a pair of c.o. relay contacts to provide direction control

how little you intend to automate the layout. If manual direction control is all that is required, simply use a DPDT switch instead of the relay contacts.

The voltage and current ratings of relay coils are generally too high to permit them to be driven direct from a logic output. However, a simple relay driver of the type shown in Figure 3.12 is all that is needed to permit a logic output to control practically any low voltage d.c. relay. This is just a simple common emitter switching stage. D1 suppresses the high reverse voltage that would otherwise be generated across the relay coil each time it switched off. Do not omit this component, as these high voltage transients could cause a lot of expensive damage.

Although a 12 volt supply is specified in the circuit, there should be no difficulty in using a 15 volt supply. Relay coils can operate properly over quite wide voltage ranges. The relay's

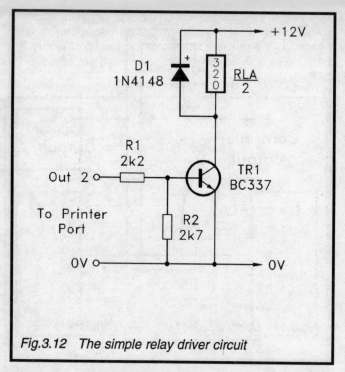

Fig.3.12   The simple relay driver circuit

coil resistance should be about 250 ohms or more. The circuit should work perfectly well using a six volt relay if the supply voltage is reduced to an appropriate level. If you use a relay having a six volt coil is should have a coil resistance of about 125 ohms or more.

When using a motor speed controller plus the direction control circuit it is obviously necessary to have nine output lines (eight for speed control and one for direction control). There is no major problem when interfacing to a PC printer port, since there are four handshake output lines in addition to the eight normal data outputs. Problems only arise if these lines are needed for other purposes, such as controlling model signals.

It is possible to provide speed and direction control from an eight bit port, but seven bit resolution has to be accepted for the speed control circuit. In practice this will still give something like a hundred different speeds, which provides quite fine speed control. This permits smooth acceleration and deceleration of a model train with no obvious jumping from one speed to the next.

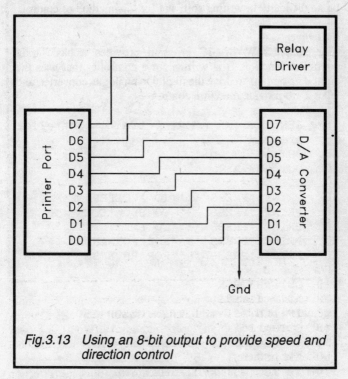

Fig.3.13   Using an 8-bit output to provide speed and direction control

The basic method of using an eight bit port for both types of control is shown in Figure 3.13. The general scheme of things is to have the lower seven bits of the port drive the upper seven inputs of the digital to analogue converter. There is no output available to drive the least significant input of the converter which is therefore connected to earth. This reduces the maximum output voltage to 2.54 volts, but this is not of any real importance in practice. The most significant output is free for use with the direction control relay driver circuit.

With this system values from 0 to 127 provide speeds from zero to maximum. Adding 128 to a value provides the same speed, but reverses the direction of the motor. For example, 32 provides a low speed in one direction, while 160 (32 plus 128) provides the same speed in the opposite direction. There should be no difficulty in writing software for this method of control.

Software

This simple GW BASIC program provides a basic train controller function. It is written for a controller that uses the eight data outputs to drive the digital to analogue converter, and "Out 2" to provide direction control.

```
10    REM  A/D  Converter  train  controller
      program
20    OUT &H378,0
30    OUT &H37A,0
40    CLS
50    PRINT "PRESS '1' TO ACCELERATE"
60    PRINT "PRESS '2' TO SLOW DOWN"
70    PRINT "PRESS '3' TO END"
80    PRINT "PRESS 'F' FOR FORWARDS"
90    PRINT "PRESS 'R' FOR REVERSE"
100   X = 0
110   OUT &H378,X
120   A$ = INKEY$
130   IF LEN(A$) = 1 THEN GOSUB 150
140   GOTO 110
150   IF ASC(A$) = 49 THEN X = X + 5
160   IF ASC(A$) = 50 THEN X = X - 5
170   IF ASC(A$) = 51 THEN END
180   IF ASC(A$) = 114 THEN OUT &H37A,4
190   IF ASC(A$) = 102 THEN OUT &H37A,0
200   IF X > 255 THEN X = 255
210   IF X < 0 THEN X = 0
220   RETURN
```

The first few lines simply set the start-up conditions, with the train stopped and set to the notional forward direction. Lines 40 to 90 print instructions on the screen which tell the user which keys to press for various actions. Lines 110 to 140 provide a continuous loop which monitors the keyboard. If a key press is detected, the program branches to the subroutine at lines 150 to 220. Depending on which key is pressed, the subroutine increments or decrements the value of "X" (the value written to the converter), alters the direction setting, or brings the program to a halt. Lines 200 and 210 keep the value of "X" within the acceptable limits of 0 to 255. The value of "X" is incremented and decremented by five per loop, simply because I found that incrementing and decrementing one at a time gave very sluggish control. With a fast PC increments and decrements of one would probably give better results.

One advantage of using a computer for this type of thing is that sophisticated control can be provided using very basic hardware. For example, simulated inertia, momentum, and braking can be implemented by software routines, and do not require any additional hardware. It is well worthwhile experimenting a little with various methods of software control.

Pulsed Controller

A computerised constant voltage controller will provide quite good results, but there is clearly some advantage in using a pulsed controller. Whether the train is "driven" manually or by the computer, the superior control characteristic provided by a pulsed controller is likely to give more realistic results.

With a computer based system it is possible to provide pulsed control using some very simple hareware. Basically all that is needed is an amplifier and buffer circuit driven from a digital output of the computer. The computer rather than the hardware generates a pulsed signal having suitable mark-space ratios. Figure 3.14 shows the circuit diagram for a suitable amplifier/buffer stage.

IC1 operates as a voltage comparator having a reference potential of about 1.7 volts fed to its inverting input by R2 and R3. The digital output port drives IC1's non-inverting input. R1 provides static protection when the circuit is not connected to the PC. TR1 provides buffering at the output so that the high currents required by the motor can be supplied. With the digital output low, the non-inverting input of IC1 will be below the reference level, and the output of the circuit will drop to 0 volts.

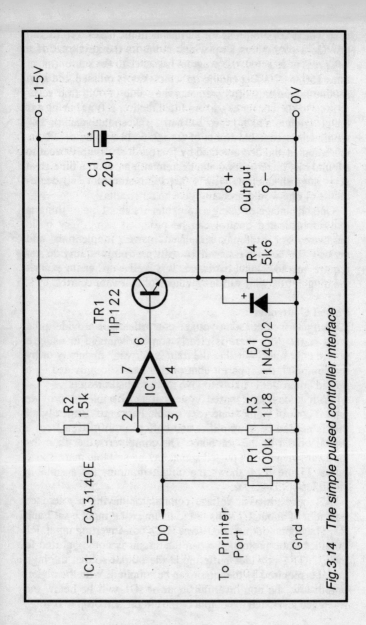

Fig.3.14 The simple pulsed controller interface

Taking the digital output high results in the non-inverting input of IC1 going above the voltage at the inverting input, and the output of the circuit then goes to about 12 volts or so.

As this circuit is a pulse type it produces relatively little dissipation in the output device. However, I would still recommend using a heatsink on the output device. A type having a rating of about 9 degrees celsius per watt should suffice, but it might be safer to use a slightly larger heatsink (say about 6 degrees celsius per watt) for a controller that will drive a two amp motor. Remember that the heat-tabs of the TIP121 and TIP122 connect internally to the collector terminal, and use an insulating kit where appropriate.

Software

Generating accurate mark-space ratios at a frequency of a few hundred hertz is something that really requires a fairly fast programming language. However, this GW BASIC listing will give reasonable results with a fairly fast PC (at least a 33MHz 80386 processor).

```
10    REM Software generated pulse
      controller program
20    OUT &H378,0
30    CLS
40    PRINT "Press 'a' to accelerate"
50    PRINT "Press 'b' to brake"
60    PRINT "Press 's' to stop program"
70    PRINT "Press 'f' for forwards"
80    PRINT "Press 'r' for reverse"
90    H = 50
100   L = 50
110   OUT &H378,1
120   FOR HIGH = 1 TO H:NEXT HIGH
130   OUT &H378,0
140   FOR LOW = 1 TO L:NEXT LOW
150   A$ = INKEY$
160   IF LEN(A$) = 1 THEN GOSUB 180
170   GOTO 110
180   IF A$ = "a" THEN H = H + 1
190   IF A$ = "a" THEN L = L - 1
```

143

```
200   IF A$ = "b" THEN L = L + 1
210   IF A$ = "b" THEN H = H - 1
220   IF A$ = "s" THEN END
230   IF A$ = "f" THEN OUT &H37A,0
240   IF A$ = "r" THEN OUT &H37A,4
250   IF H < 1 THEN H = 1
260   IF L > 100 THEN L = 100
270   IF L < 1 THEN L = 1
280   RETURN
```

There are two basic approaches to pulse control. The more sophisticated method is to have the mark (high) period decrease as the space (low) period decreases, and vice versa. This gives the required changes in average output voltage, but gives a more or less constant output frequency. The more simple method is to have a fixed mark period, and vary the space time. This still enables a wide mark-space ratio to be produced, but gives a broad range of output frequencies. The method used here is to have complementary changes in the mark and space times so that the output frequency remains virtually constant.

Lines 30 to 80 clear the screen and then print a series of on-screen instructions. The next two lines set the variables "H" and "L" at an initial value of 50. It is the values of these variables that respectively control the high and low periods of the pulsed output signal. The FOR . . . NEXT delaying loop at line 120 produces the mark period, and the second FOR . . . NEXT loop at line 140 controls the space period. Initially variables "H" and "L" are equal at a value of 50, giving a roughly one-to-one mark-space ratio, and an average output potential of about half the supply voltage.

Pressing a key takes the program into the subroutine, and if an appropriate key is pressed, the value of "H" and "L" will be stepped up or down in increments or decrements of one (lines 180 to 210). Lines 250 and 260 keep the values of "H" and "L" between 1 and 100. This represents an approximate range of mark-space ratios from 100 to 1 at full power to 1 to 100 at minimum power. The actual range is likely to be slightly less than this in practice due to the time taken for some lines of the program to be executed. However, the range of mark-space ratios obtained is sufficient to give very good results with most electric motors.

Line 220 brings the program to a halt if the "s" key is pressed. The forward/reverse switching (if implemented) is provided by lines 230 and 240.

This program is written on the basis that the controller circuit is connected to printer port 1, the buffer amplifier is driven from data output D0, and the forward/reverse switching is controlled via handshake output "OUT 2". If you use a different setup it will be necessary to amend lines 20, 110, 130, 220, and 230 accordingly.

Components for Figure 3.14

Resistors (all 0.25 watt 5% carbon film)

R1	100k
R2	15k
R3	1k8
R4	5k6

Capacitor

C1	220µ 25V elect

Semiconductors

IC1	CA3140E
TR1	TIP121 or TIP122
D1	1N4002

Miscellaneous

Case, circuit board, 8-pin d.i.l. holder, 25 way male D type connector and two-way lead, multi-strand connecting wire, solder, etc.

P.W.M. Control

An alternative method of providing pulsed control is to use a conventional pulse width modulation (p.w.m.) controller, fed from a digital to analogue converter. This type of circuit is controlled in exactly the same way as a constant voltage controller, but the output signal to the motor is a pulsed type.

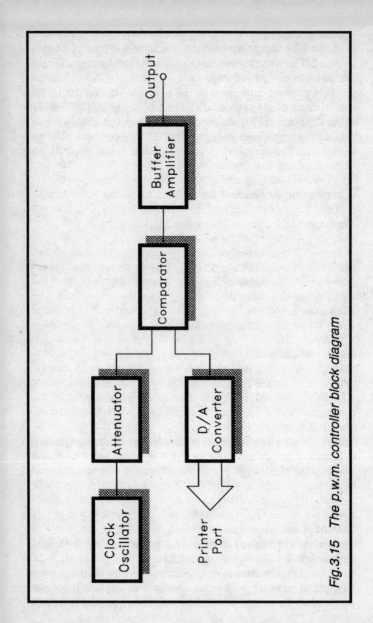

Fig.3.15 The p.w.m. controller block diagram

This method clearly requires more hardware than a software based pulse width controller, and is substantially more expensive to implement. It does have a potential advantage though. This is simply that the computer is not having to use up a large percentage of its time generating an output signal having the correct mark-space ratio. The computer merely outputs values to the digital to analogue converter, and leaves the hardware to generate the appropriate output signal. This permits accurate control using rudimentary software. Furthermore, there is no need to use a fast programming language or a fast PC. Because very little of the computer's processing time is occupied undertaking the basic control of the train, it is possible to undertake sophisticated automatic control of the train. Again, this does not require the use of a fast programming language or the latest thing in go-faster PCs.

Figure 3.15 shows the block diagram for the pulse width modulation controller. The voltage comparator is at the heart of the circuit. It has one input (usually the non-inverting input) fed with the output voltage of the digital to analogue converter. The other input is fed with an attenuated clock signal. It is essential to the operation of the circuit that the clock signal is a reasonably good triangular type. In an application of this type a high degree of linearity through the system is not really needed, so a few imperfections in the clock signal are tolerable.

With zero output voltage from the converter the clock signal will always be at the higher potential, and the output of the comparator will always be low. A small output voltage from the converter will result in the clock signal being at the higher voltage for the majority of the time. The output of the comparator is therefore pulsed at the clock frequency, but will be low for the majority of the time, giving a low average output voltage. If the output voltage from the converter is increased, the clock signal will be higher than the input voltage for a lesser proportion of the time. This gives a higher average output voltage. If the output voltage of the converter is taken high enough, it will always be higher than the clock voltage, and the output of the comparator will go high continuously.

In practice the attenuator is adjusted so that the maximum and minimum clock voltages are just within the output voltage range of the converter. This enables the average output voltage to be set at zero, the full supply potential, and a wide range of intermediate levels. A buffer amplifier at the output enables the circuit to supply the high output currents required by a small d.c. motor.

P.W.M. Circuit

The digital to analogue converter circuit for the p.w.m. controller is exactly the same as the one for the constant voltage controller (Figure 3.9). The circuit for the rest of the p.w.m. controller appears in Figure 3.16. The clock oscillator is based on IC2, which is a dual operational amplifier. It is used in a conventional triangular/squarewave oscillator of the type which uses an integrator (IC2a) and a trigger circuit (IC2b). In this case only the triangular output signal from IC2a is required. C4 and R4 are the timing components, and these set the clock frequency at around 300 to 400Hz.

The output signal from IC2a has an amplitude of about 9 volts peak-to-peak, which is clearly far larger than the level of about 2.5 volts peak-to-peak needed at the input of the comparator. Also, the minimum clock voltage is about two volts, rather than the required potential of little more than 0 volts. VR1 is used as a variable attenuator which reduces the peak-to-peak amplitude of the clock signal to a suitable figure, and it also reduces the positive offset. D1 to D3 introduce a voltage drop of about 1.8 volts or so which also helps to take the positive offset down to an acceptable level.

IC3 is an operational amplifier, but in this circuit it functions as the voltage comparator. TR1 is the output buffer stage, and it is a power Darlington device used in the emitter follower mode. R7 acts as its load resistance with no external load connected across the output. D4 suppresses any reverse voltage spikes generated across the highly inductive loading provided by a d.c. electric motor.

Like TR1 in the simple pulsed controller interface, TR1 in this circuit should be fitted with a small heatsink. This circuit is controlled in exactly the same fashion as the constant voltage controller. VR1 must be given a suitable setting if the unit is to work well. Start with the wiper of VR1 at the bottom end of its track. With a value of 255 written to the digital to analogue converter, advance VR1 just far enough to give full speed from the

148

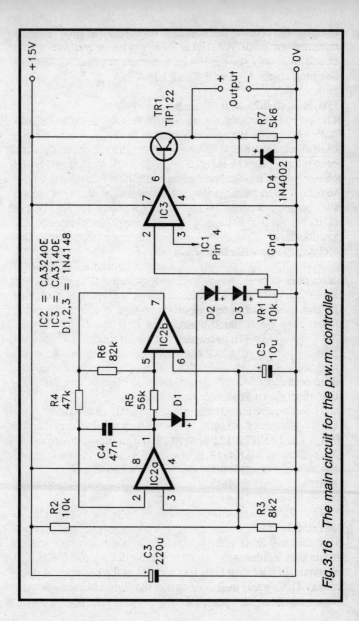

Fig.3.16 The main circuit for the p.w.m. controller

model train. The system should then have a good control characteristic.

Components for Figures 3.9 and 3.16

Resistors (all 0.25 watt 5% carbon film)
R1	390R
R2	10k
R3	8k2
R4	47k
R5	56k
R6	82k
R7	5k6

Potentiometer
VR1	10k min preset

Capacitors
C1	4µ7 63V elect
C2	22µ 16V elect
C3	220µ 25V elect
C4	47n polyester
C5	10µ 25V elect

Semiconductors
IC1	ZN426E
IC2	CA3240E
IC3	CA3140E
TR1	TIP121 or TIP122
D1	1N4148
D2	1N4148
D3	1N4148
D4	1N4002

Miscellaneous
8 pin d.i.l. holder (2 off)
14 pin d.i.l. holder
Heatsink for TR1 (see text)
25 way D plug and lead
Case, circuit board, solder, etc.

5 Volt supply

Several of the circuits featured in this chapter require a +5 volt
supply. This could be obtained via a mains power supply unit,
but it is easier and cheaper to obtain this supply from the PC.
The +5 volt supply is available from the PC's expansion bus,
but where the computer is fitted with a joystick ("games") port,
this provides the easiest access to a +5 volt output. Figure 3.17
provides connection details for the PC joystick port. There are
four +5 volt outputs available, and it does not matter which one
is used. The connection to the joystick port is made via a male
15 way D type connector.

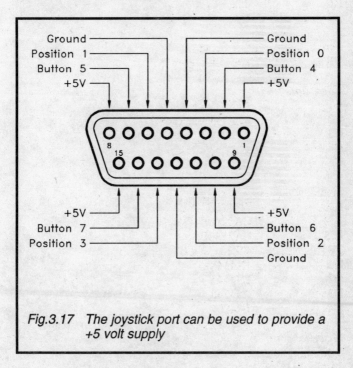

*Fig.3.17 The joystick port can be used to provide a
+5 volt supply*

151